Government and virtues

This is a fine plant of the sun. The dried fruit, as it comes from abroad under the name of raisins, and currants, is good in coughs, consumptions, and other disorders of the breast. The leaves of the English Vine boiled, make a good lotion for sore mouths: if boiled with barley meal into a poultice, it cools inflammation of wounds: the droppings of the vine, when it is cut in the spring, boiled with sugar into a syrup, and taken inwardly, is excellent to stay women's longings when pregnant. The decoction of the leaves in white wine, does the same: or the tears of the vine, drank two or three spoonfuls at a time, breaks the stone in the bladder. The ashes burnt (the) branches make discoloured teeth white by rubbing in the morning. It is the most gallant tree of the sun, very sympathetical with the body; that is the reason why spirit of wine is the greatest cordial among vegetables.

Culpeper's 17th Century,
"British Herbal".

Growing Grapes in Britain

—a hand book for winemakers
and viticulturists

Written and illustrated by

GILLIAN PEARKES

1969

1973

SBN 900841 09 5

First Edition   1969

Second Edition   ..   1973

Published by: The Amateur Winemaker, South Street, Andover, Hants

Printed by: Standard Press (Andover) Ltd., South Street, Andover, Hants
Telephone 2413

Contents

Illustrations

LOVE

All love at first, like generous wine,
Ferments and frets, until 'tis fine,
But when 'tis settled on the lee,
And from the impurer matter free,
Becomes the richer still, the older,
And proves the pleasanter, the colder.

Samuel Butler
1612-1680

Introduction

WINEMAKING is now one of our most popular national pastimes, and it is only to be expected that many who have taken up the hobby have also toyed with the idea of growing their own grapes for the purpose.

Grapes produce the ultimate in wine, and contrary to popular and widespread public belief in this country are easily grown and regularly ripened out of doors in most areas of Great Britain. Disbelief of this arose from failures when would-be growers were sold varieties of vines that were cold or hot-house cultivars by ignorant and misleading nurserymen. Such varieties will never succeed without the protection, heat and lengthened season afforded by a glass-house. This iniquitous practice is still in operation, most comprehensive plant catalogues still recommend indoor varieties for outdoor use, and on radio programmes the "experts" stubbornly adhere to similar recommendations. It is not until we can educate these so called authorities that belief in the success of viticulture in this country can be established.

This book is not a scientific journal, but rather a practical handbook on how to grow vines successfully in the open, on walls and fences, and in glass-houses to produce grapes for making wine and grapes for the table. Therefore, there is a noticeable absence of masses of scientific data, and to make the subject more easily digestible there are plenty of diagrams to explain certain details more readily.

The book has been written both for the amateur gardener who wishes to grow a few vines in the back garden and for the aspiring private or commercial viticulturist who may have anything from a hundred to thousands of vines in mind, the problems which have to be met are exactly the same. There is a great revival of practical interest in viticulture in the British Isles, constituting a real need for this book; there have been a very few works printed on vinegrowing during the past decade, and invaluable books these have been, but in general each has been written from a definite angle covering just one of the many aspects with which we are concerned with here; indoor vine growing, the commercial size vineyard approach, and others from the experimental results obtained from many differing varieties on a certain site.

This work has been based upon the experiences and obstacles I have met and overcome during the establishment and fruition of my two experimental vineyards in Devon. I have had as many varieties here on trial as possible, to discover which types of vine will regularly crop and ripen their crop in this area. This information only becomes interesting when compared with the data so generously compiled and sent by other enthusiasts from all corners of the British Isles; it is only from such a jigsaw collection of records that one can build up a reliable picture on recommending specific varieties for different areas. This data is further supported by the map which I have compiled showing the sites of these existing experimental plots and the larger private and commercial vineyards. My grateful thanks are hereby extended to my many vinegrowing friends and correspondents without whom this section would be non-existent.

Surely to read that man has grown vines successfully within the nearby district of an aspiring newcomer would be more of an incentive than reading of the achievements of some far-off vineyard in Devon or Sussex or some other seemingly ideal corner; a good many eyes are opened when they realise that vines can be grown outside in most parts of England, thanks to the importations and exhaustive trials on hundreds of varieties by the early pioneering efforts of the renaissance of English vinegrowers.

THE ZODIAC.   William Lilly of London, 1659

"Christian Astrology, Modestly Treated Of In Three Books"

Aquarius.   20 January - 18 February

This sign gives more beauty than any other besides Libra, ... gentle, benevolent ... governs illness in the legs, ankles, veins ... delights in being on water, in vineyards.

CHAPTER 1

Where can vines be grown in the open in the British Isles ?

TO begin with we must explode one or two widely held opinions, categorical statements made by the "know alls" whenever the subject of growing vines is mentioned in day-to-day conversation. They loudly contend that it is quite impossible to grow vines in Britain, and that therefore any idea of actually ripening grapes in such a climate as ours would be sheer lunacy, thus labelling anyone who attempts to argue with them an absolute fool!

To shatter this myth, one need only look into the past and collate such evidence as can be found on the subject of English viticulture. That this country has had a long and obviously successful courtship of the vine, and has evidently benefited from her favours for some 1,800 years should be some foundation for wanting to join the ranks of those dedicated to re-establishing the vine once more within our shores.

To elucidate further: we can go back to the Roman Emperor, Domitian, who decreed in A.D. 85 that all vineyards beyond the bounds of Italy were to be scrapped. Luckily for us this edict was later rescinded by the Emperor Probus in A.D. 280, permitting vines to be planted in Gaul, Spain and Britain.

The first recorded vineyard in Britain was probably in the grounds of a Roman Villa named Vindomis, which forms an interesting link with the mansion later built on this site in the

16th Century and known as The Vyne, first owned by Lord Sandys. One may suppose that many of the more favourable situated Roman villas were quick to follow suit, and could soon boast a vineyard. It is known that the Romans introduced the vine into this country, certainly by the time the Venerable Bede wrote his Ecclesiastical History of England, (*circa*. 734), they were an accepted crop of sufficient note for Bede to state "Britain . . . also produces vines in some places . . ." amongst his descriptions of other crops, domestic and wild animals and natural amenities.

A century later Alfred the Great (849–901) stated in his laws " . . . that compensation shall be paid at an exact valuation by anyone damaging the vineyard or field of another . . ." such evidence proving beyond doubt that vines were a commonplace and accepted part of the country scene.

When William the Conqueror took over, he ordered a vast and complete survey to be made of the people of Britain, their houses and lands, and here we find no less than 38 established vineyards recorded. In the Domesday Book most vineyards were in Somerset, Essex and South Suffolk, whereas a century or so later Worcestershire and Gloucestershire were the main centres of vinegrowing.

The earliest vineyards were in general connected with monasteries, due to the fact that monasteries sprang up after the Norman invasion and were mostly manned by French and other Europeans who had had some considerable previous experience in the culture of the vine. They liked to keep up their previous culture and habits, and the growing of vines and drinking of wine was an inherent part of their very existence. One can assume that most monasteries had a vineyard; the interest soon spread to the Norman land-owner Barons, and many large estates sported a vineyard until the decline came in about 1350.

This waning in practical participation was due principally to four factors, firstly, the climate changed for the worse for a time at this period resulting in cloudy, wet summers caused by direction changes of ocean currents. Secondly, just prior to this time a great part of the French and Portuguese vine lands came under British rule, and remained so for some 300 years; much French wine therefore flooded into this country

14

and displaced the home product. In 1348–9 one third to a half of the population of England succumbed to Bubonic plague, or the Black Death as it was later named, and fourthly the English vine varieties were mostly unsuitable, and ripened too late in the now poorer summers.

The English vineyards suffered their most serious setback when the monasteries were sacked by Henry VIII in the 16th Century, but a few dedicated enthusiasts continued to carry the flag through the centuries as will be seen in the list of vineyards of the past.

A revival of interest was shown in the 18th Century when many of the great houses and their accompanying gardens were built, owners vying with one another to have as much or more than their rivals in the features of their house and grounds.

The last of the vineyards was planted by Mr. Pettigrew for the Marquis of Bute at Castle Coch in Glamorgan in 1875, followed by a second at Swanbridge near Cardiff. The 1914–18 war brought to an end to these enterprises, and saw the end of the long era of British vinegrowing which began with the Romans.

Some 30 years later, in 1946 and 1948 respectively, Mr. Barrington-Brock and Mr. Edward Hyams started vineyards, thus reviving viticulture again in Britain, and in the comparatively short time since their early efforts there has been a tremendous revival of theoretical and practical interest in the vine in this country, so much so that there are now 430 acres, nearly 150 established commercial vineyards, in existence, and many more being planned; moreover, there are between one and two hundred private vineyards of varying sizes now well established.

The reason for this fast growing enthusiasm is the range of new varieties of vine that are available, that have come from the research stations of Germany and France, enabling us to expect the certainty of a ripe harvest each and every year. Many hundreds of these modern strains were tested and tried at the Oxted Viticultural Research Station, and 24 or so successful varieties emerged from these experiments, thus enabling us to start a viticultural venture on a sounder footing than the early vinegrowers, who had to struggle on with most unsuitable and irregular ripening vines. Had they been able to start with the advantages open to us there would surely have been no decline, but a steady rise in the numbers of vineyards resulting in this country being a recognised vine-growing area today.

However, perhaps it is more exciting for us, participants in the vanguard of the new wave of viticulture in Britain, to have the task of proving to ourselves, to our own countrymen, and perhaps to the world that we are capable of making wine of a quality on a par with that of France and Germany.

THE ENGLISH VINEYARDS ASSOCIATION

The English Vineyards Association was formed in 1966 to cater for the interests of both the commercial and amateur vinegrower, and from small beginnings has an ever growing membership that stands today at well over 300. The E.V.A. has done much to gain recognition of the re-birth of English wine production both in Government and Ministry of Agriculture circles, and has acted on our behalf in E.E.C. discussions. An annual symposium is held, also a tasting of English wines followed by a luncheon is arranged each September, and more important members are well circularised on current trends in new vine varieties and methods of cultivation. The Secretary's address is Mrs. J. G. Barrett, The Vineyards, Cricks Green, Felsted, Essex.

THE SOUTH WEST VINEGROWERS ASSOCIATION

was formed in 1970, and by early 1973 collected over 80 members, one quarter of whom grow commercially within the area. Some six events are arranged annually, including a one day course at Long Ashton Research Station, Bristol, and visits to commercial and private vineyards. Hon. Sec. Miss Pearkes, Rhyll Manor, Dulverton, Somerset.

Before discussing the areas where vines are grown and can be grown in Britain today, let us glance through a few of the vineyard sites of the past ...

16

List of some of the known early vineyards

(Note: 1 Arpend = 1.25 Acres).

County	Site	Date	Owner	Area
Bedfordshire	Dunstable			
Berkshire	Abingdon Bitesham Wallingford Castle WINsore (Windsor)	Domesday	Monks of Abingdon Henry de Ferrieres	12 Arpends
Cambridge-shire	Denny Abbey		Abbots	
Devon	Colyford Colyton, Kingsdon Allotments Colyton, Southleigh Colyton, Willhayne Honiton, Coombe, Gittesham	c. 1814	2 French brothers	
Derbyshire	North WINfield South WINfield WINgerworth			
Dorset	Bridport, Loders, Bridport, Shipton Gorge			
Essex	Belcamp Edelsfort Hedingham Castle Great Waltham Ragencia	Domesday Domesday	Alberic de Ver Sweyn, a Dane Aubreyde Vere Geoffrey de Mandeville	11 Arpends 6 Arpends 10 Arpends 6 Arpennies
Gloucestershire	Tortworth			
Hampshire	Basingstoke Beaulieu Abbey Vineyard Holm WINchester	Roman 1240		
Hertfordshire	Boxmoor Dunstable Hatfield Ware	Roman 1605	Robert Cecil, 1st Earl of Salisbury	30,000 vines 6 Arpennies
Isle of Ely	Church of Ely (named L'Isle de Vignes by Normans)		Bishops of Ely	
Isle of Wight	St. Laurence	1792	Sir Richard Worsley	

County	Site	Date	Owner	Area
Kent	Canterbury Abbey	1285	Abbots of St. Augustine	
	Canterbury Priory Canterbury	1285	Osbertus de Vinea	
	Godrington, Great Chart		Captain Nicholas Toke	
	Great Chart		Sir Peter Ricard	
	Rochester, Halling	1325	Bishop of Rochester	
	Rotherhithe Sevenoke(sevenoaks) (Sevenoaks)			
Lincolnshire	Spalding Priory		Prior John	
Middlesex	Chenetone Holbourne (Holborn) Westminster	1084 Domesday 1084	Bishops of Ely	
	Blackheath Brompton Coldbath Fields Hammersmith Hatton Garden		Colonel Blunt Mr. King	
	Holborn Houndsditch	1295	Earl of Lincoln	
	Kensington Piccadilly Trinity Church, London Vine Street		Dr. Shaw Earl of Essex	
	Wimbledon, and after at Chelsea	1783	Francis Xavier Vispre	
Northampton-shire	Peterborough	1135–1184	Abbot Martin	
Oxfordshire	Oxford, Trinity College	1685	Dr. Ralph Bathurst	
	Tame, (Thame)?		Baron Tame	
Somerset	Bath		3 commercial vineyards of a farmer of Bath	
	Bath, Claverton	1742	Sir William Bassett	
	Dunster Castle Glastonbury, Wirral Hill			
	Pilton Abbey	1235	Vineyard cared for by William Aurifabie	
Staffordshire	Over-Arley (Over-Ashby or Upper Arley)?	after 1300	Sir Henry Littleton	

County	Site	Date	Owner	Area
Suffolk	St. Edmundsbury (Bury St. Edmunds) Sudbury Priory	Roman	Abbots	7 acres
Surrey	Cobham Godalming (Vineyard Hills) Oatlands Pains Hill	1586 1604 1760–1790	Lord Cobham James I The Hon. Charles Hamilton	
Sussex	Santlac, Battel (Battle)	Norman Invasion		... "a great store of vines"
	Arundel Castle	1763	Duke of Norfolk	"a noble vineyard"
Worcestershire	Abberton Allesborough Hill	12th and 13th centuries		
	Brushley	12th and 13th centuries		
	Doddenham Priory	until 1240		
	Droitwich Fladbury, Worcester Priory	until 1240	Abbots	
	Grimley	until 1240		
	Hallow Priory Hampton	1084	Monks of Evesham	
	Leigh	12th and 13th centuries		
	Pershore, Hunger Hill			
	Severn Stoke	12th and 13th centuries		
Wiltshire	Hantum Lacock Abbey Wilcote	1229		
Yorkshire	Asham, York Abbey		Abbots	
Wales	Glamorgan, Castle Coch	1875–1914	Marquis of Bute	20 acres
	Glamorgan, Swanbridge	–1914	Marquis of Bute	9 acres
?Hoxton		18th century	Thomas Fairchild	
?Waltham Green		1790	Bartholomew Roque	

There was also a vineyard at Bisham, at Chaddesley, where there were two vineyards in 1290, and further vineyards were sited at Raleigh.

Vineyards in Britain today

Today, nearly 30 years since the renaissance of modern viticulture, we are most fortunate in the now vast range of vine varieties available to us from the Alsatian, German and Swiss Viticultural Research Stations. Most of these vines are bred from the noble European vinifera varieties, (see chapter 2 for a list of these vines). The greater adaptability of this new race of vines enables wine growing to be embarked upon with the certainty of success in ever increasing areas of England.

Commercially, the greater the area planted with vines, the better the value and use of the machinery and vineyard equipment. As a rough guide, adopting the traditional Guyot method of training, (see chapter 4), 2,200 vines are needed per acre planted at $4' \times 5'$ or $5' \times 5'$ spacings. If a full size tractor and trailer are to be used, then 10′ avenues will be needed between the rows. Spacing is therefore geared to equipment at hand, or the equipment to be purchased.

On average a vineyard vine will yield 3 lb. of grapes per annum, and planted along traditional $4' \times 5'$ lines some 2,000–3,000 bottles of wine per acre may be expected from a mature vineyard in a good year.

A fair proportion of the newer vineyards are following the methods practised by Austrian Dr. Lenz Moser, who advocates 10′ wide avenues, and planting the vines 10′ apart. The vines are trained up a high trellis so that all work is at face level, the grapes are borne at this height which simplifies care and saves time. If cropping potential is not lowered by having a mere 500 vines to the acre, if the grapes ripen with a satisfactory sugar content, and if enough replacement wood ripens being five foot above the warm reflective properties of the soil, and mildew problems are reduced, then this revolutionary method will be here to stay. We shall see.

How do we define a vineyard? The dictionary states that a "vineyard is an enclosure for grape vines; a plantation of vines for producing grapes." How many vines do there have to be in a plantation to constitute a vineyard? The dictionary does not elucidate here. To make a hard and fast rule, and say, for example, that the figure of 100 vines would be the fewest that could be classed as a vineyard would instantly rule out the great number of very keen experimental vine-growers who grow a great variety of vines though not necessarily in any quantity. The results they obtain are just as valuable as the results submitted by the grower of a great many vines, more so in fact, if the large vineyard grows but one variety of vine.

There follows a county by county gazetteer listing where vines are being grown today in Britain. The vineyards mentioned are those known at the time of going to Press; there are obviously more in existence about which information would be much appreciated.

A proportion of the vineyards in the following report were too immature to have produced a crop yet, but even so it is interesting to know of their whereabouts, the varieties planted and other details. There are other smaller plantations, but one cannot obviously include every vine in existence, the line has to be drawn somewhere. The published data have been chosen for inclusion due to the interest value of the results obtained in relation to the area concerned. I think it will come as a surprise to many to discover just how many vineyards there are in the British Isles.

GAZETTEER OF ENGLISH AND WELSH VINEYARDS

The first figure in the acreage column represents the area planted at the time of publication, the second being the proposed final acreage.

Commercial Vineyards

Name, Location of Vineyard	Height	Address	Varieties	Planted
BERKSHIRE				
Astor, the Hon. J. Vineyard at Coombe	650′	4 acres	M. Thurgau S. Villard	1970
Cardy, W. L., Pangbourne		3–9 acres	M/T, S/V	1967
Hole, G. B., Bradfield	200′	4½ acres	M/T, S/V	1969
Howitt, Mrs. A. Finchampstead		pilot plot	Reich, Marien	1962
McLean, G., Abingdon				1974

Name, Location of Vineyard	Height	Acreage	Varieties	Planted
BERKSHIRE—*continued*				
Theobald, B. H., Purley, Reading	120'	9–14 acres	M/T, S/V	1970
Vaughan-Morgan, Miss I., Finchampstead		3 acres	Mariensteiner	1972
BRISTOL				
Houghton, J. D., Stapleton	150'	2·5 acres	M/T, S/V, M/A	1972
University of Bristol, Long Ashton Research Station	200'	½ acre	many	1965
CAMBRIDGESHIRE				
Reece, G. P., Gamlingay		6–9 acres		1972
Basham, A. H. and Partners, Waterbeach		¼–6 acres		1973–4
CORNWALL				
Baker, D. V., St. Buryan, Penzance		1–2 acres	M/T	1973–4
Brown, A. E., Calstock		¼ acre	M/T	1973
Coburn, N., Roseworthy, Camborne	50'	4½ acres	M/T, S/V, M/A	1969
Littlewood, P., St. Juliot Miles, J. N., St. Mawes, Truro	200'	200 vines	M/T, S/V, M/A	1969
Stone, H., St. Keverne, Helston	200'	1–15 acres	M/T, Reich, Mar	1973
Weaver, J., St. Breward, Bodmin				1973
Woodacre, R. W., Talland Bay, Looe		¼–5 acres	M/T, M/A, Chass	1972
CHANNEL ISLANDS				
Guernsey				
Grayson, Talbot Valley		½ acre	M/T, S/V	1966
Jersey				
Blayney, R. H., St. Mary		1–5 acres		
DEVON				
Forbes, A. E. and partners, Broadclyst, Exeter	200'	3–7 acres	M/T, S/V, M/A, Huxel	1969
French, T. M. J., Stoke-in-Teignhead	400'	1–3 acres	M/T	1970
Macdonald, N., Tiverton	400'	¼–5 acres	M/T, M/A, Scheurebe	1973
Morland-Coon, J. R. H., Knowle, Sidford	100'	2–5 acres	M/T, P/Chard	1974

22

Name, Location of Vineyard	Height	Acreage	Varieties	Planted
DORSET				
Scrimegour, J. H., Lychett Matravers		1–5 acres		1974
Waters, K. N., Merley, Wimborne	150'	5 acres	M/T, S/V	19 1 –2
ESSEX				
Barrett, J. G. and I. M., Felsted	220'	10½ acres	M/T, S/V and others	1968
Crocket, Dr. R., Bergholt		1 acre	Reich, Perle	1970
Ernst, F. C., Weeley Heath, Clacton	70'	½ acre	M/T, S/V, M/A	1970
Fisons, Saffron Walden		½ acre	M/T, Chass	1966
George, C. E., Colchester		4 acres		1970
Greenwood, S. W., Purleigh, Chelmsford		5–10 acres	Reich, Perle	1970
Jeffries, R. V., Saffron Walden	400'	2 acres	M/T, S/V	
Langham, Fruit Farms, Langham		2 acres	M/T	1973
Norris, H., Enfield		½–1 acre		
Soldani, A., Billericay		2 acres		
Williams, W. A., Colchester		2 acres		
GLOUCESTERSHIRE				
Bowley, K., Ashton Keynes, Cirencester		5 acres	M/T, M/A. P. Chardonnay	1972
HAMPSHIRE				
Bird, M. J., Ringwood		1½–3 acres		
Gore-Brown, Mrs. M., Beaulieu		5½ acres	M/T, S/V, W/Pinot	1961
Salisbury-Jones, Major Gen. Sir Guy, Hambledon		4½ acres	M/T, S/V, P. Chard, Pinot Noir, etc.	1952
Suter, C. D., Rowlands Castle,		5½ acres		
Walter, A. D., Hayling Island		5 acres		1973
Wright, J., Ringwood		½–2 acres		
HEREFORDSHIRE				
Fisons, Ross-on-Wye		¼ acre		1970
James, K. R. H., Bodenham		1–5 acres		
Marcon, R. B., Ledbury		1-5 acres		1974
Possnit, C., Clyro		5 acres		
HERTFORDSHIRE				
Latchford, P. G., Frithesden		2–3 acres		1972

Name, Location of Vineyard	Height	Acreage	Varieties	Planted
ISLE OF ELY				
Sneesby, N. J., B.A., M.S., Wilburton	50–70'	2– acres	M/T, S/V, P/Chard	1972
ISLE OF WIGHT				
Barlow, K. C., Adgestone	200–400	8½ acres	M/T, S/V	1968
Poulter, W. N., and Gibbons, R. H., Cranmore, Yarmouth	100'	4–6 acres	M/T	1967
KENT				
Bates, T., Nettlestead	50'	3 acres	M/T, S/V, S/13053	1967
Barnes, R. A., Biddenden	400'	8¼ acres	M/T, S/V, S/13053	1969
Cave, J. A., Goudhurst		5 acres		
Cooper, R. D., Peckham, Maidstone		1¾ acres		
Grant, I. A., Ulcombe, Maidstone	425'	¾–1½ acres	M/T	1969
Grover, Mrs. L., Downe		½–¾ acre		
McAlpine, K., Tunbridge Wells		8–15 acres		1972
Richmond, Throwley, Faversham		1–6 acres		1972
LINCOLNSHIRE				
Rook, Major A., Lincoln		1¾ acres	M/T, S/V	1964
NORFOLK				
Carey, Mrs. D. E., Fressingfield		2–3 acres		
Cohen, C. H., Burnham Market	40'	1–14 acres	M/T, S/V	
Day, Mrs. P. H., Hoxne, Diss	147'	2–10 acres	M/T	
Don, R. S., Elmham, Dereham		¼–5 acres	M/T, S/V, Perle	1967
Hannah, Mrs. N. H., Hempnall				1972
Hunter, D., Dereham		1–3 acres	M/T	1973
Milkovitch, J., East Harling	150'	1 acre	M/T	1972
Roger, J., Hempnall				1972
Rowlands, A. D., Marsham				
Thorpe, J. W., Starston				
Woodrow, D. H., Topcroft				
SHROPSHIRE				
Furness, J. F. G., Bridgenorth		2 acres		

Name, Location of Vineyard	Height	Address	Varieties	Planted
SOMERSET				
Bell, K. G., Thornbury Castle		1–2 acres	M/T	1970
Gillespie, Major C. L. B., Shepton Mallet		2–5 acres	M/T, S/V	1970
Godden, N. de Marsac, Pilton, Shepton Mallet		4½–15 acres	M/T, S/V, Rulander	1967
Dible, S., Limington, Yeovil		1 acre		1972
Roberts, V., Cheddar		¼–3½ acres		1974
SUFFOLK				
Abbot, C. C., Cockfield				1972
Ambrose, B., Cavendish	120'	10 acres	M/T	1972
Bird, B., Laxfield		7 acres	M/T	1973
Bolton, K. E. R., Wetheringsett		1–5 acres	M/T	1972
Bunn, M., Woodbridge		5–16 acres	M/T	1971
Campbell, C., Darsham		4 acres	M/T	1973
Cartwright-Abbott, C., Bury St. Edmunds		½–8 acres	M/T, S/V	1972
Cary, T., Fressingfield	165'	3 acres	M/T	1973
Clarke, C., Otley, Ipswich		6 acres	M/T, Pinot Blanc	1973
Debenham, D. G. and H. B., Burgate				1972
Edgerley, J. T., Kelsale, Saxmundham		1 acre		
Fitzgerald, K. and White, J., Suffolk Vineyards, Cratfield		7–10 acres	M/T, P/Noir, P/Chard	1972–3
Fuller, Mrs. M. Y. and Mr. M., Wickhambrook, Newmarket	450'	5–10 acres	M/T	1973
Gardner, R. T. T., Framlingham	160'	14 acres	M/T	1973
Grove Park, Yoxford	130'	1½ acres	P/Chardonnay	1972
Hope, M., Barningham, Bury St. Edmunds		5 acres	M/T	1972
Milburn, P., Sibton		¼ acre	M/T	1973
MacFarlane, I. W. M., Saxmundham		½–1 acre		
Norris, H., Deben Valley Vineyard	25'	1,400 vines	M/T, S/V, M/A	1969
Powney, G., Botesdale	130'	17 acres	M/T, S/V, etc.	1972
Rawlinson, C., Brampton		3 acres	M/T	1973
Sims, P. J., Hepworth		5–10 acres	M/T	
Simpson, Cdr., Bury		4 acres		
Smith, E. C., St. Lawrence, Beccles	145'	1½ acres	M/T, S/V	
Wills, Wills & Lawry, Wortham	90'	4 acres	M/T	
Seckford Bridge Hotel, Woodbridge		¼ acre	M/T	1972–3–4

Name, Location of Vineyard	Height	Acreage	Varieties	Plante
SURREY				
Baillie-Grohman, T. P., O.B.E., D.S.C., R.N., Hascombe, Godalming	400'	6–7 acres	M/T, S/V, etc.	1968
Melstrom, G. J., Godalming		¼ acre		
Ockley Vineyard Co., Ockley		3½ acres	M/T, S/V, S/13053	1967
Pratt, R. V., Ottershaw, Chertsey				
SUSSEX				
Carr-Taylor, D., Westfield, Hastings		4–12 acres		1972
Cowderoy, N., Haywards Heath	250'	2 acres	M/T, Hux, Rieslaner	1965–6
Crossland-Hinchcliffe, J. C., Plumpton Green, Lewes	170'	2 acres	M/T, S/V, Reich	1967
Evans, H., Arundel		5 acres		
Hollamby, Mrs. P., Burwash		pilot plot		
Merrydown Wine Co., Horam		3 acres	M/T, M/A, and others	1968
Moray, A. P., Ticehurst	320'	1½–5 acres	M/T, Pinot Noir	1973
Paget, I. & A., Singleton, Chichester		6–12 acres		1963
Parigo Horticultural Co., Chichester		2½ acres	Rembrant	1966
Parker, T. B. L., Alfriston		2 vineyards		
Pratt, Mrs. J. M., Bolvey		3–5 acres	M/T	1973
Royce, H., Heathfield		2 acres		
Smith, Mrs. P., Fletching Common	150'	1¼ acres	M/T	1963
Stansfield, W., Playden, Rye	100'	½–1½ acres	M/T	1972
Thorley, D., Broad Oak, Rye	100'	1¼ acres	M/T, S/V, W/Pinot	1963
Tollemache, N., Uckfield		8 acres	M/T, Hux, Reich	1973
WILTSHIRE				
Bowley, A. K., Ashton Keynes		8 acres		
Donald, J., West Tytherley	230'	1½–5¾ acres	M/T, M/A, T/A, S/13053	1968
WORCESTERSHIRE				
Roland, R., Evesham		proposed 5 acres	M/T	1973–4
WALES				
Pembrokeshire				
Mathias, Wing Cmdr. L., Lamphey Court		2½ acres	M/T, S/V, Seibel	1962

Private Vineyards

Name, Location of Vineyard	Height	Acreage	Varieties	Planted
BERKSHIRE				
Elliot, Dr. J., Henley-on-Thames				
Ford, P. P.		450 vines	M/T, S/V	1967
Nowell, Mrs. J., Frilsham	400′	1 acre		1969
BRISTOL				
Hender, R. O., BS9 3RY		120 vines		
Hudd, K., BS15 3JB		30 vines	10 varieties	1965
Pollard, Dr. A., O.B.E., Backwell		36 vines	S/V, W/P, Seibel	1954
Watson, R., Stoke Bishop		50 vines	M/T, S/V, Seibel	1971
Wishart, J.		25 vines +	S/V, M/A, etc.	1958
BUCKINGHAMSHIRE				
Sichel, P., Chalfont St. Peter	300′	100 vines	Riesling, S/V	1968
CAMBRIDGE				
Youngman, Dr. H. R., Cambridge	40′		many varieties	1964
CORNWALL				
David, J., Calstock		33 vines	M/T, S/V, M/A	1970
Hood, O., Looe	200′	200 vines	M/T, S/V, etc.	1967
Miller, Mrs. J., Stoke Climsand	400′	300 vines	M/T	1972
Wilson, D., Treen, Penzance	100′	⅓ acre?	S/V, Seig, etc.	1972
DEVON				
Barber, G., Torrington		50 vines	M/T, M/A, P/Ch, etc.	1971
Bexter, J., Chudleigh		¼–3 acres	M/T	1973
Clarke, M., Stoodleigh, Tiverton	800′	75 vines	M/T	1973
Cockshutt, R., Skilgate, Bampton	800′	1–5 acres?		1974?
Comfort, A. J., Bishops Nympton	600′	20–300 vines	M/T, M/A	1973–4
Coyle, Brig. D., Barnstaple	400′	100 vines	M/T, S/V, M/A	1972
Crighton, D., Lapford, Crediton	200′	200 vines	M/T, Sheurebe	1973
Crompton, Sqn. Ldr. D. M., Parracombe	4–600′	pilot plot	many varieties	1972–3
Davenport, C. J. H., Kingsbridge		100 vines		
Davis, Abbotsham, Bideford	50′	500 vines	S/V, M/Syl	1971
Downes, Greensheilds, Major T.M.J., Hawkchurch, Axminster	350′	30 vines	M/T, S/V, M/A	1968

27

Name, Location of Vineyard	Height	Acreage	Varieties	Planted
DEVON—*continued*				
Kemmis, P. W., Ivybridge		100 vines		
Lobban, K., Woodleigh, Kingsbridge	180'	½ acre	M/T, S/V	1973–4
Newton, Miss S., Dunsford, Exeter		35 vines		1971
Pearkes, Miss G. G. Rhyll, Dulverton	825'	½ acre	M/T, M/A, Sheu, etc.	1970
Pond, Prof. D., Bridford		30 vines		1973–4
Rayner, G. T., Paignton	425'	¼ acre	30 varieties	1963
Scott-Elliot, Miss A. M., Totnes	300'	100 vines	M/T, S/V, etc.	1971
Smythes, J. H., Dartmouth	80'	71 vines	M/A, M/S, Seibel	1962
Spurway, M., Hawkchurch	325'	1–8 acres	M/T, S/V, M/A, etc.	1964
Wallace, H., Sheepwash		100 vines	M/A, M/S, Seig, etc.	1964
Wimpeney, Halwill, Okehampton	500'	¼ acre	M/T	1973
DORSET				
Bagnall, C. F. R., Cerne Abbas		100 vines	M/T, S/V	1970
Chadwick, V. J., and Lawrence, J. E. C., Thornford, Sherborne		½ acre	M/T, Scheurebe	1973
Glover, T. J., Milton Abbas		½ acre	"	1973–4
Harmer, R. A., Shaftesbury		¼ acre	M/T, S/V, Sheu	1970
Partridge, R. B., Tarrant Weynston		pilot plot	M/T, S/V	1972
Scrimgeour, J. H., Lychett Matravers		1–5 acres?		1973–4
Wingfield Digby, J., Blandford	200'	½ acre	M/T, S/V	1969
ESSEX				
Evans, E., Saffron Walden		½ acre		
Hamilton, E., Rayne, Braintree		50 vines		
Harding, P., Saffron Walden		200 vines	M/T	1973
High Birch Poultry Farm, Clacton		½ acre		
Perry, H. H., Chadwell St. Mary		27 vines		1960
Ramsey, C., F.R.H.S., Billericay	150'	1–60 acres	M/T, M/A, M/S, etc.	1965
HAMPSHIRE				
Burgess, K. G., Petersfield	200'	235 vines	M/T, S/V, M/S	1964
Montagu, Lady, Blackfield, Southampton	40'	0·5 acre	M/T, S/V, W/P	1964
HEREFORDSHIRE				
Snell, G. L., Much Birch		300 vines		

Name, Location of Vineyard	Height	Acreage	Varieties	Planted
KENT				
Colegrove, Mrs. E., Hawkchurst		100 vines		
Corfe, J. M. B., Sevenoaks		160 vines		
Grose, B. R., Beckenham		30 vines		
LEICESTERSHIRE				
Hanger, R. H., Anstey, Leicester		50 vines +	28 varieties	
LINCOLNSHIRE				
Lincoln Cathedral		200 vines		1972
NORFOLK				
Ashbolt, M., Wymondham	150′	½–½ acre	M/T, S/V	1970
Stennet Wilson, R., Bale-Fakenham	144′	½ acre	M/T, S/V, Seibel	
Symington, I., King's Lynn	20′	180 vines	M/T, S/V, Ort, Ries	1972
NORTHAMPTONSHIRE				
Lewis, N. L., Kingsthorpe		48 vines	11 varieties	1962
Hart, Sir W., Brackley		36 vines	M/A, M/s	1966
NOTTINGHAMSHIRE				
Houghton, J., Langar		85 vines	M/S, Seig, Seibel	1967
Durant, D. N., Bleasby, Nottingham		31 vines	S/V, Seibel	1967
SHROPSHIRE				
Wem Modern School, Wem		100 vines	M/T, S/V, M/A, etc.	1970
SOMERSET				
Archer, R. E., Bridgwater		100 vines	many varieties	1969
Aunger, R. B., Charlton Radstock	400′	300 vines	S/V, M/A, Seibel	1965
Cleeve Priory, Watchet	100′	100 vines	W/Pinot	1973
East, L. H., Chaffcombe, Chard		40 vines		
Packer A., Cheddar		300 vines	M/T, M/A, Seibel	1972
Pennell, N., Kilmersdon		½ acre		1971
Pinnington, A., Tuttons Hill, Cheddar		½ acre	M/T, Gewurtz	1973
Primavesi, F. A., Combe Down, Bath	150′	?		1973–4
Roughton, C. H., Dunkerton, Bath		1½ acres	M/T	1973–
STAFFORDSHIRE				
Monkton, Mrs., Stafford		200 vines		

Name, Location of Vineyard	Height	Acreage	Varieties	Planted
SUFFOLK				
Blackie, J., and Blair, M., Little Cornard, Sudbury		200 vines	M/T, S/V, M/A, etc.	1970
Hansom, E. H., Ipswich		150 vines		1971
Milborn, Cdr. P., Sibton	120′	300 vines	M/T	1971
Sheepshanks, Capt. R. J., Eyke		?		
SURREY				
Cornwell, K. H., Nutfield		1 acre		
Filby, E. G., Croydon		90 vines	15 varieties	1960
Hornblow, A. J. D., Bookham		50 vines	M/T, S/V	1968
Imeson, H. E., Epsom		50 vines	M/T, etc.	
Warner, M. R., Guildford	425′	1 acre	S/V, Gamay	1956
Whittaker, Dr. J. F., Guildford	200′	98 vines	S/V, M/A, Seigerrebe	1966
SUSSEX				
Clark, G. D. D., Brighton	100′	30 vines	M/T, S/V	1967
Cyster, R. J,. Northiam, Rye	70′	½ acre		1972
Elliott, E. McC.,		90 vines		
Parker, T. B. L., Roedean		⅔ and 1 acre		
House, J., Littlehampton		70 vines		
Rickman, J.		25 vines		1971
WARWICKSHIRE				
Adams, F. D., Cook Hill, Alcester		185 vines		
George, F. F., Bidford-on-Avon		200 vines		
Higgins, T. F., Hall Green, Birmingham 28		120 vines		
WILTSHIRE				
Bradford, L. W., Great Cheverall	200′	¼ acre	M/T, S/V, M/A, etc.	1970
Carlisle, D. E., Crockerton, Warminster		50 vines	M/T	1973
Chivers, L. R., Potterne, Devizes		50 vines	M/T, M/A, Seibel	1972
Henry, Dr. S., Hilperton	200′	200 vines	M/T, T deAl, Seib	1968
Howley, T., L.D.S., Winsley	300′	140 vines	M/T, Seibel	1962
Osborne, Col. G. E. R. C., Seend		¼ acre	M/T, M/A, Seibel	1963

Name, Location of Vineyard	Height	Acreage	Varieties	Planted
WORCESTERSHIRE				
Barrett, Rev. D., Kidderminster		50 vines		1973
Bowen, R. F., Redditch		270 vines	M/T, S/V, M/A, etc.	1964
Bye, P., Woolastone, Stourbridge	360'	1½ acres	S/V, M/A, Seig, etc.	1966
Harford, Sir T., Evesham		25 vines	M/T, S/V, Seibel	1966
Anon, Nr. Worcester		130 vines	M/T, S/V, Seibel	1964
Rodgers, D. F. J. T., Warley	700'	100 vines	M/T, S/V, M/S, etc.	1962
WALES				
Cardiganshire				
Higgins, T. F., Ystrad Meurig and at Hafod	500'	195 vines	M/T, S/V, M/A, etc.	1968
Manooch, Mrs. M., Llandyssul		175 vines	M/T, S/V, Seibel	1966
Sherwood, R., Llanrhystud	50'-100?	½-1½ acres	M/T, S/V M/A	1973
Thomas, Dr. G. I., Llanarth		1,069 vines	M/T, S/V	
Carmarthenshire				
Brown, D.	500'	a vineyard		
Gore-Brown, Mrs., Trimsaran		1,100 vines		1962
Jones, Mrs., Cwm, Pembrey		400 vines	M/T, S/V, Seibel	1963
Kenrick, R. S., Henfwlch Road, Carmarthen		100 vines	M/T	1973
Reynolds, Mrs. D., Cwm-ffrwd		300 vines	M/T, S/V, Seibel	1963
Williams, T. G., Craig, Burryport		315 vines	M/T, S/V, Seibel	
Glamorganshire				
Jones, H. G., Dinas Powis		300 vines		
Lloyd, W. G., Llanelli		120 vines	M/T	
Salter, B., Cowbridge		100 vines		
Tantagliam, P., Llanelli				
Hawkins, Mrs., Oxwich		100 vines		
Monmouthshire				
Eastor, H. W., Penarth				
Lenza, P., Abergavenney				
Llewellyn, Col. Sir G., Tredilian Park		small vineyard		
Lomas, P. J., Newport				
Powell, J., and Morgan, R., Monmouth		1 acre	M/T	1972

Name, Location of Vineyard	Height	Acreage	Varieties	Planted
Pembrokeshire				
Gore-Brown, Mrs. M., Lamphey, Pembroke		1,000 vines		1962
Thomas, Dr. D. L., Pembroke		1,000 vines +		
EIRE				
Co. Cork				
Weale, L. N., Kilworth		½ acre		1973

EXISTING VINEYARDS

Diagram 1.

X,½ acre –
Kilworth,
Co. Cork,
Eire.

KEY
Commercial Vineyards ●
Private Vineyards ✕
150 + Commercial Vineyards
150 + Private Vineyards
Copyright Gillian Pearkes 1975

CHAPTER 2

Outdoor vines for English wine production

PRIOR to the coming of Phylloxera from America in 1860, only native vines of the area were grown in Europe, these being known as Vitis Vinifera.

When the vineyards of Europe struggled to their feet after the ravages of Phylloxera, this was by means of grafting scions of the v. vinifera on to rootstocks of vigorous American vines. Within the past 50 years a new range of vines has evolved resulting from artificial pollination of v. vinifera with the American v. Labrusca, v. Rupestris and v. Riperia, resulting in the modern hybrids.

Vitis Vinifera and the Hybrids

The advantages of the Euro-American hybrids became immediately apparent: they were Phylloxera-resistant, like their American parent, they were lime tolerant, and virtually mildew resistant.

With such advantages, these vines seemed the obvious answer to everyone's prayers, but as with most revolutionary discoveries, one or two drawbacks gradually became evident. Firstly the quality of the wine was poorer by far than that from pure European vines. The plants cropped more heavily and the wines matured faster, but they lacked that all-essential character.

Hybrid vines are now banned from any European vineyards holding or seeking "Appellation Controlée" status for their products. An English vineyard seeking the equivalent, a certificate denoting quality control and a high standard of production, must abide by the same restriction now that we are to compete both in England and on the continent as members of the European Community.

To sum up, hybrids are fine for the private or amateur enterprise, particularly for those sites where mildew is endemic, where trouble free vine culture is essential, and where a quantity, as distinct from a quality product is acceptable. Where, however, quality is the aim, particularly on the commercial scale, where consistently high-class wine is the key to continued sales, hybrids are definitely out.

Finally, one can readily appreciate from the vine variety list that follows that there is now no shortage of pure vinifera cultivars, bred from the noble vines of Europe by the modern German, Alsatian and Swiss Viticultural Research Stations; and the choice grows annually as newer types become available to us.

Recommended

VINE VARIETIES FOR THE OPEN VINEYARD: Vitis Vinifera WHITE

(parentage in brackets)

MÜLLER THURGAU

Müller Thurgau, (Riesling Sylvaner), the latter indicating the parentage of this vine, has been planted in more English Vineyards over the past fifteen to twenty years, and in greater numbers, than any other vine. This is due to the fact that until recently its performance, growth rate, and high quality grapes have been better than that of any other vine available to us, and has become a standard with which we tend to compare all other vines, particularly the newer vines bred by the German Research Stations. Müller Thurgau is by no means perfect, being vulnerable to mildew attack as the grapes approach ripeness, but it has been indisputably the best quality vine to date. The name derives from the breeder, a man named Müller who lived in Thurgau in Switzerland. It is hereafter abbreviated to M.T.

MÜLLER THURGAU

This vine grows well, needs good weather during pollination, and requires regular preventative spraying, being susceptible to both Botritis and Oidium. Cropping ratio: 2–4 tons per acre, the golden-brown grapes ripening by mid-October. Makes an excellent Alsatian type wine of considerable quality and bouquet, which matures early due to low acidity.

ALBALONGA: New (Sylvaner × Riesling) = (Rieslaner × Sylvaner)

Vine can be too vigorous, a prolific cropper which ripens at the same time and yields at the same rate as M.T. Sugar content always high, 80–90 oe., wine being fruity and elegant with great breeding, slow to mature and keeps well. Prune to 2 long arched canes

ARIS: New

Mildew resistant, yield low, sugar 120°-140° oe.

AUGUSTE LUISE: New

BACCHUS 133: New. Sylvaner × (Riesling × Müller Thurgau)

Vine habit very similar to M.T., but more reliable in flowering, yield 4–5 tons per acre, quality therefore probably lower, acidity higher. Wine flavour attractive, with a hint of muscat.

DOMINA: New

EHRENFELSER: New (Riesling × Sylvaner)

Growth fairly vigorous, yield lower than M.T. Must attains 5°–10° oe. higher than Riesling with similar acidity. Fruit ripens a week prior to Riesling, providing a fruity, mature wine of Riesling type.

FABER: New (Weissburgunder × Müller Thurgau)

Faber needs a good site, but is tolerant of a wide variety of soils producing 3–4 tons per acre. Fruit ripens earlier than M.T., sugar 80°oe., higher acidity of 0.8–1 % than M.T. Attractive fruity flavour, wine should be superior to M.T.

FORTA 100: New (Madeleine Angevine × Sylvaner)

Forta requires a good site, can cope with dry soil and is very hardy against winter frost. Crops 2–3 tons per acre, gives a high sugar content, high acidity, providing fruity wines not unlike Riesling.

FRIESAMER: New (Sylvaner × Rulander)

Likes almost any soil, does well on good sites, but susceptible to coulure. Harvests 2–3 tons per acre, sugar and acidity higher than M.T., wine flavour reminiscent of Pinot Gris, (Rulander).

GEWURZTRAMINER

This is the same vine as Traminer, but supposedly an earlier clone. A noble grape, and together with Sylvaner, Muscat, Pinot and Riesling makes the better wines of Alsace, totalling a third of the country's total vinous output. Sets and ripens its crop earlier than Riesling. May well be too late in England except in a super year, but worth a trial.

HUXELREBE: New (Gutedal × Court Musque)

Needs a good to medium site, well drained soil, growth more vigorous than M.T. Produces 2–3 tons per acre which can vary according to pollination conditions. Often necessary to develop two fruiting canes, does not like chalk, affected by both mildews and stem rots unless adequate precautions are taken. Fruit ripens ten days earlier than M.T., Sugar and acidity well above M.T., so should produce a top quality muscat flavoured wine.

JUBILAEUMSREBE: New (Portugieser blau × Blaufraenkisch)

A new Austrian variety which is regularly producing Beeren-auslese in Austria with oe. readings averaging 132° over a period of 12 years on one site. If readings are below 125° wine can have an unsatisfactory flavour; will only blend with a few varieties.

KANZLER: New (Müller Thurgau × Sylvaner)

This vine needs a good position, wood does not ripen easily. Oe. 88.5°, acidity 0.50–0.70. Harvest mid-October, wine of fine fruity flavour, superb quality.

KERNER: New

Ripens wood well, delicious light flowery wine.

MADELEINE ANGEVINE 7972

A German vine of very fair vigour, cropping more heavily than M.T., ripening earlier, though more prone to mildew as grapes ripen. Wine of good quality, when fermented right out, slight muscat flavour. Suitable for less favourable areas.

MADELEINE SYLVANER 28/51

Another German cross, of medium vigour, harvest lighter than M.T., very prone to botritis but producing a light high quality wine of Alsatian type. Worth trying on less favourable sites as this grape ripens very early indeed, mid to late September on a good site.

MARIENSTEINER: New. Sylvaner × (Sylvaner × Riesling) = Rieslaner)

A vigorous vine, good pollination, hardy; prune to 2–4 short canes, needs a good site. Plant 4″ × 5″ at least. Bud burst later than Sylvaner, wood ripens earlier, less susceptible to Spring and Autumn frosts. Yield 2–3 tons per acre. High S.G. 80–90 oc. High acidity. Quality higher than M.T., being as full bodied as a mature Sylvaner, spicy refined soft bouquet, reminiscent of meadow flowers. Matures slowly.

MORIO MUSCAT
A vine of above average vigour, a heavy cropper of large bunches, culture straightforward. Needs a warm situation, but ripens later than Scheurebe. In some seasons cropping potential low.

OPTIMA 133: New
Yield low, clusters small, a rich generous wine.

ORTEGA: New (Müller Thurgau × Seigerrebe)
An aristocrat, which is however apt to poor pollination. Prune to long canes in double arcs sharply inclined towards the ground. Yield 2–3 tons per acre. Ripens 2 to 3 weeks prior to M.T., sugar and acidity higher so quality expected to be superior. Wine neutral and harmonious, soft muscat peach bouquet, attaining 80°–90? oe.

PERLE: Wurtzberger Perle (Gewürztraminer × Müller Thurgau)
This vine, produced by Dr. Brieder, can stand minus 35°C in winter, and minus 6°C in spring when the sap is actually rising. Sensitive to botritis, grapes ripening a little after M.T. Abundant cropper, modest sugar and low acidity levels. Wine very light, delicate, soft and flowery, matures early, early consumption recommended.

PINOT CHARDONNAY
A member of the finest family of grapes, responsible in France for the production of Champagne, Chablis and Montrachet, which is gaining some interest in England now it is realised that it will in fact ripen here.

PINOT GRIS: (also known as Rulander)
An Alsatian Pinot, the wine having less bouquet than Muscat, but more body and distinction. This vine is gaining interest in England, and being planted in several vineyards, an interesting newcomer with obvious potential if successful. Sometimes known as TOKAY.

PRÉCOCE de MALINGRE
A vine of poor vigour, and of close, shrubby habit which might tend to attract mildew, difficult to train. Produces small crops of well ripened fruit of good colour ripening early. Yield 1 ton per acre, wine non Muscat, fresh and pleasant.

RABANER: New
Grown on Mosel, short vegetation, wine 10° oe higher, acidity lower than M.T., wine light, fine and green like a Moselle.

RAMDAS: New

REGNER: New (Luglienca bianca × Gamay Frueh)

This vine likes good quality porous soil, NOT chalk, and a good site. Susceptibility to downy mildew no worse than M.T., powdery mildew no problem. Grapes start to ripen a week prior to M.T., harvest a few days later, 80°oe. in Rheinhessen, acidity 1%. Wine aromatic, spicy, slightly muscat.

REICHENSTEINER: New (Müller Thurgau × (Madeleine Angevine × Calabresser Frohilch))

A medium site and a fairly rich soil needed, tendency to botritis slight, vulnerable to stem rot, wood ripens late, akin to M.T. Medium to strong growth, yield 2–3 tons per acre. S.G. 5°–10° higher than M.T., acidity 0.1–0.2% higher. Wine has a full bodied flowery character, and is highly recommended.

RIESLANER: New (Rhine Riesling × Franconian Sylvaner)

Ripens 2 weeks prior to Riesling on good to average sites, produces a really fine wine with all the characteristics of the original Riesling.

RIESLING

This is one of the noble vines of Europe producing wines of great quality in Germany and Alsace, and is the parent or grandparent of most of the newer vines listed here. It has until now been thought too late to ripen in the open in England, but is certainly worthy of trial on the best sites where it could well ripen more years than not; enabling the grower to producer top class wine.

SCHEUREBE: (Sylvaner × Riesling)

A vine of considerable quality, bred by Herr Scheu, requiring a favourable site, doing well in well drained soil yielding 2–3 tons per acre. Wine blends well with M.T. and S.V., and has an attractive bouquet. A highly recommended vine for English wine production, cropping more heavily and ripening 10 days earlier than Riesling, having a much greater volume of bouquet.

SCHONBURGER: New (Also known as Rosa Muskat)

Cultivation of this variety is much simplified due to good behaviour at flowering, and adaptability to soil and conditions. Wine is full and fruity, 80°-100° oe, excellent flavour.

SEIGERREBE: (Madeleine Angevine × Gewurztraminer)

This cultivar tends to be temperamental during flowering, likes a good site, but not chalk. Of medium vigour, ripens wood well. Grapes harvestable by late August, early September, therefore open to wasp attack. Suitable therefore for later or less than perfect sites. Yield 1½–3 tons per acre, high sugar content, low acidity; powerful flavour and bouquet lend the grape to dessert wine production. Bred by Herr Scheu.

SEPTIMER: New

TRAMINER: (see Gewurztraminer)

TROLLINGER × RIESLING: New

Suitable for sparkling wine production, worthy of trial in England to see how well it will ripen.

WURZER: New (Gewurztraminer × Müller Thurgau) (Also known as Wuerzer and Wartberger)

A fairly vigorous vine with early budbreak, mildew prone. Prefers a neutral soil, fertile and well aerated, and a fairly good site. Fruit ripens 3–4 days prior to M.T., wood ripens well. Yield 2½–3 tons per acre, 80°–90° oe., acidity 0.7%–0.8%. Wine has a powerful flavour akin to Gewurztraminer.

Black varieties vitis vinifera

KOLOR: New (Blauer Spätburgunder × Teinturier)

No preference for special soil, but in common with other black varieties the best site available is required here. Grapes are good for colour rather than quality, yielding 2–3 tons per acre.

NOIR HATIF DE MARSEILLES

Not a strong grower, requiring a richer soil than most, very early ripening consistent cropper, fair yield, slightly muscat flavoured.

PINOT NOIR

This vine requires a really good site and well drained soil, and is one of the best French Burgundy grapes, and is also used in Champagne production. Yielding some 2–3 tons per acre, it should produce a degree of quality if blended with white or red wines, worthy of trial.

WROTHAM PINOT

Reputedly originally imported and grown in England by the Romans, this vine was re-discovered some twenty years or more ago in Kent. This sojourn in England has resulted in this clone of *Pinot Meunier* ripening some two weeks earlier than its brother. A vine of excellent vigour and habit, Wrotham Pinot is producing some very good sugar readings in Essex, and is recommended for red or white wine production; a light to medium cropper ripening at about the same time as M.T.

ZWEIGELT REBE (Blaufrankisch × St. Laurent)

A variety praised in Austria and elsewhere; is well worthy of trial in well drained favourable sites. Yield 2–2½ tons per acre, wine colour is acceptable, but body somewhat light, might blend well with Pinot Noir.

Hybrid vines   White

EXCELSIOR

A French hybrid of medium vigour with light cropping potential.

SEYVE-VILLARD 5/276

A vine of medum vigour and easy habit, slow to grow early in the season, and prone to coloure if lime is not added every April/May on an acid soil. Suitable on chalk. A heavy cropper, 3–5 tons per acre, but sugar readings are usually low to medium and acidity high. A thin wine of little character compared to M.T., a quantity rather than quality wine. Rootstock 5BB, or 41B for chalk soil.

Hybrid vines   Black

BACO I

A rampant grower better suited to covering a large area of building or wall than in the open vineyard where multiple cordon training is recommended. A heavy cropper, wine coarse and rank when young, but after some years mellows to a fairly pleasant beverage. Entirely mildew resistant.

PIROVANO 14

A strong-growing medium cropper of fair quality grapes.

SEIBEL 13053

A vine of apparently weak growth, but a consistent mildew and disease free grower, light to medium cropper producing a red wine of little quality. Grape juice is red, useful as a stain for red wines.

TRIOMPHE d'ALSACE

A vigorous mildew and disease free vine, heavy cropper producing a better red wine than other hybrids. Very early ripening, consistent and entirely trouble free.

Other vines grown in England . . .

Listed here are some vines not grown on vineyard scale, but mostly on walls and in small experimental batches in the open vineyard. In most cases the reasons for this are given.

ASCOT CITRONELLE: An early ripening golden muscat grape of inconsistent habit.

BLUE PORTUGESE: Probably needs more sun than we can offer in the open, ripens on walls in Bristol.

CHASSELAS ROSE, d'OR and 1921: A standard eating grape in France, this variety is too late for the **open** vineyard here; however on walls it will ripen large crops of superb quality fruit that make a very good wine of Champagne character and bearing. Recommended highly.

FOCH: A black French hybrid that ripens early, mildew and trouble free, but has not attracted much attention here.

GAMAY HATIF des VOSGES: French, black, shy cropper.

GREY RIESLING: Ripens much too late for English summers.

GRENACHE: A black French grape of fine quality, also grown in Australia, and South Africa. Probably too late for this country.

LEON MILLOT: Another black French hybrid, due to hybrids tending to be phased out in England, this vine arrived too late to catch on.

MADELEINE ROYALE: A white grape of very inconsistent habit. Walls only.

MARSHAL JOFFRE: A black French hybrid, very early ripening, like Millot and Foch.

MESLIER PRÈCOCE: Not recommended, needing more sun than we can supply.

MUSCAT DU SAMUR: An early muscat golden grape, inconsistent cropper. Walls only.

OBERLIN BLACK 595: This vine has not caught on due to better varieties. Beautiful autumn leaf colouring.

PEARL de CZABA: White muscat, weak grower, producing small bunches.

PINOT MEUNIER: Too late without cloches, Wrotham Pinot better by far.

STRAWBERRY: (black and pink) An excellent wall grape ripening a large crop of strawberry flavoured grapes by mid October, makes good eating, but an undistinguished wine. Of American origins.

SYLVANER: Probably too late for England, this quality Alsatian white grape is on trial in one or two vineyards where results are awaited with interest.

American vines grown in England

In the eastern state vineyards of America native vines of the continent are grown, namely Vitis Labrusca, Riperia and Rupestris; a few that have emigrated to England are listed here. The resultant wines tend to be of "foxy" flavour, and as such are in general distasteful to the English palate. The vines are however, interesting to grow and compare with v. vinifera.

ALDEN: A good grower, disease free, mostly inconsistent cropper here.

BRANT: A Canadian vine of vigour, suitable for growing on walls where it ripens a large crop of tight black bunches, beautiful autumn foliage.

BROCTON: This variety produces sweet grapes of good flavour.

CAMPBELL'S EARLY: Appreciates light soil, produces large attractive bunches.

CONCORD: This is the leading commercial variety in the New York state vineyards, needs walls or cloches, and has beautiful red foliage.

EMERALD: Ripens consistently in open vineyard, superb green wine grapes.

HIMROD SEEDLESS: The only seedless grape grown so far, good flavour, cloches recommended.

SCHUYLER: Ripens a medium crop of black grapes by early November, recommended.

SLADE BLUE: Grows well in Cambridge, can be a shy cropper. European v. vinifera varieties are grown in the Californian vineyard.

Russian vines grown in England

Circulation of these Russian vines is limited, but from the few reports to hand they appear to be early ripening, prolific, producing small berries, but have not been planted on a vineyard scale to date. Amongst those being grown in England are **Gagarin Blue, Kuibishevsky** and **Tereshkova**.

CHAPTER 3

Planting in the open

BY planting vines in the open it is meant that one is considering the possibilities of whether one has a site suitable for planting vines in an open garden or field situation as opposed to planting vines against a wall or fence. Instructions on growing vines in walls is given in a later chapter.

Before deciding where you would rather have the vines it is as well to assess the points for and against the site you have to offer; if it is less perfect, can any improvements be wrought to make the prospect of growing vines successfully more of a certainty? Follow this by an assessment of your soil structure, and decide whether any adjustment will be necessary to provide a better growing medium for the new tenants. Let us now go through these three important points in more detail before going further.

A perfect site is a southerly or a south-westerly slope, this is for obvious reasons; the first being better and longer exposure to the rays of the sun each day, warmer soil and better growth rate, and also a warm slope provides that all important efficient drainage of surface and sub-surface rain water.

Very few sites are in fact, perfect and usually much can be done to improve the possibilities. The first consideration is to attract as much sun as is available, for without sufficient the vines cannot absorb enough sun through the leaves to ripen the grapes fully. If there is a tree or hedge that hinders the rays of the sun try to have this obstacle removed.

Frost precautions

Another important consideration in the siting of vines is the danger of spring frost. Frosts are not harmful during the autumn or winter, and indeed are beneficial in that they kill insect pests and mildew spores; without hard, cold weather the vines do not have a good season of rest and are apt to rush into leaf too early.

Frost rolls down the hill sides taking the line of least resistance such as valleys and inclinations, and eventually pools in the valley or basin bottoms, forming what are known as frost pockets. If one lives on the hillsides, which are the best positions for any fruit grower, much can be done to protect one's plantation from the dangers of the late spring frosts which are the only frosts to threaten the vines. It is only when the buds have burst and the young and tender shoots are about to produce flowers, and during the flowering period, that the frost can jeopardise the future of the crop of the current year. In good weather flowering can be over in a week or so, but if it is wet and cold, then this would well last over a time of four to five or more weeks according to the range of varieties that are grown. Hedging or other protection is fine on the upper and side peripheries of the vineyard, but one must give provision for the frost to roll on and down the hill to the valley below the vineyard. Removal of all or part of the *lower* hedge will allow the frost to continue unhindered and leave the vines unscathed. Try to imagine the frost as a heavy cloud which is aiming for the lowest local point, taking the line of least resistance and continuing to do so provided that it meets no outstanding obstacles; high thick hedges or walls form such barriers, and it tends to settle behind such a barricade until such time as it builds itself up high enough to roll over the top and continue on its downward path, leaving an extra hard pocket of frost continuously behind the obstacle in question.

If you happen to live in a frost pocket do not be disheartened, for a frost at this critical time in the vine's annual life cycle is not commonplace in this country. Flowering in a good season occurs during June; in an average year it will take place late in June or even in early July, and frosts are very unusual as late as this. All the same, to take precautions against such an eventuality, be it rare, can never come amiss.

In large orchards and vineyards the most modern method of avoiding frost damage is to sprinkle water over the vines in the evenings when frost threatens; the water then forms icicles over the vine shoots and wires and prevents the frost from killing the tender shoots and flowers. The older method was to light small fires or smudge pots at regular intervals, which kept the frost above the vine level; this again is an efficient method. For the smaller grower in the notable frost area when such a hazard is forecast, perhaps these commercially applicable methods may seem a little too difficult to effect. He will usually have the advantages of hedging, maybe walls or fences and perhaps buildings to assist him, a built up area is naturally more protected than an open valley, but nevertheless extra protection in the form of draped netting, six foot wide lengths of polythene sheeting draped over the middle wire along the rows, or even sacking or straw piled around the vulnerable canes will certainly keep the frost away. When a frost threatens at such a time, surely it is worth while to take a little trouble to prevent the loss of the entire crop?

To conclude: most sites are possible; naturally some are better than others, but do not be disheartened by the fact that all you can offer is far from perfect. Vines will grow and succeed almost anywhere within reason in this country, (see chapter 1), providing it is not too far north and too cold for an open plantation; perhaps if this is the case you might have some wall or fence space to offer with a greater chance of success?

Geographically hill tops, valley sides, open valleys, plains and plateaux offer success to the prospective viti-culturist, be the site near the sea or not. Steep sided valley or basin bottoms, being the most liable to late spring frosts, are areas where extra care might have to be taken at the one time of year in certain years when the vines are at their most vulnerable.

A really steep due northerly or easterly slope would attract too little sun to enable a vine to ripen either cane or crop, and beware of the site where the salt laden winds blow in so hard and continuously off the sea that all plants are either permanently flattened or uprooted. The North Kent coast around Herne Bay and district is in this category, and perhaps areas of the North Norfolk coast would be similar; maybe sound hedge or wall windbreaks to windward would solve this problem.

Soil assessment

Next an assessment of the soil is vital. The first move is to find out the character of both topsoil and subsoil for it is the latter through which the all important drainage either does or does not take place.

Clay soil

Clay soils present certain, though not insuperable, problems. In a clay soil, drainage is obviously poor, and vines do not prosper with permanently wet feet. This can be overcome by laying land drains beneath the surface at intervals from the top to the bottom of the site. This improves drainage immensely, but still leaves a heavy soil which hardens like concrete after being walked upon after wet weather. This condition can be improved vastly by heavy applications of partially rotted straw compost, peat and coarse sand or fine gravel which does much to increase the non-existent humus content and aeration of such a soil prior to planting the vines. This, followed by annual alternate applications of these materials will bring about a gradual permanent improvement.

During the autumn ridge the soil up against the vines leaving a furrow down the centre of the rows. This enables the frost action to attack a larger area of the soil, greatly helping to lighten and improve its condition.

Lime is an important soil beneficiary which greatly assists the weather and other additions in breaking up the heavier soils, secondly, vines prosper and grow well in a well limed soil; they retain their leaf colour, and seem to keep freer of disease. Do not apply both manure and lime together; use either one in the autumn and the other in the spring for the best results. In all but the most acid soils, lime need not be added more frequently than once in every three years. Keep the potash level high.

A clay soil is a medium which encourages strong and vigorous growth, and must therefore not be over indulged in nitrogenous matter or the vines will produce a jungle of green woody growth at the expense of fruit. Therefore the aim must be to lighten the soil, keeping a careful watch on the rate of growth and only feeding manure or compost to established vines in small doses if the vines are behaving in a restrained manner. If encouragement be needed, then with a clay soil add the compost or manure in the autumn to allow it to disperse somewhat before the sap rises in spring, and dress with lime in the spring together with any other necessary encouraging or corrective chemicals. Rootstocks: Teleki 8B, and SO4.

Lime and chalk soils

A lime or chalky soil is usually a poor, slow soil unless it has been cultivated well for a long time, but this is no drawback where vines are concerned. There are two or three varieties of vine which grow well naturally on their own roots in such a soil, but with the present choice of rootstocks available for most types of soil, the majority of vine varieties will thrive grafted on to the rootstok SO4, or for rank chalk 41B.

In common with most soils all the humus and aeration that can be introduced in the form of manure, compost and peat plus fine gravel and coarse sand are all important and should be added generously initially; thereafter use manure one year, followed by compost the next, together with any necessary chemical additions. Lime and chalk soils always drain well so there are no problems here. Some of the more successful commercial English vineyards are on chalk. Yield is not as good as from vineyards on the more generous soils, but the quality of the wine is among the best providing the vines are well fed on the lines suggested.

Loam soil

A loam soil is one of the best media for growing any crop, but a watch must be kept to insure that over nourishment does not take place or the fruiting rate will drop. The

47

best way to treat a vineyard is to follow planting instructions closely after first trying to correct any major soil deficiency or unbalance, and then wait and watch developments for a year or two before deciding on a feeding pattern. If the vines grow strongly, showing good dark green leaf colour and plenty of flower shoots, then all is well, but when this progress shows signs of falling off, then is the time to move in with the manure, compost and other beneficial aids. Loam normally needs little initial correction, merely manure and lime sparsely in alternate years, and sometimes sulphate of potash and Epsom Salts from time to time as required (see chapter 4).

Sandy and gravel soils .

Sandy and gravel soils are perfect for the vine; they drain superbly, reflect and hold the heat from the sun and encourage and enable the deep rooting which the vine loves.

Being so light, though, such a soil is quickly leached of all its goodness, some nourishment is an annual must. Plenty of manure or compost added in early spring greatly assists the production of a worthwhile crop, and helps to increase the body and general condition of the soil. Peat helps to retain moisture when the vines are young and shallow-rooted, and can either be added as a mulch or dug into the soil. Gone is the opinion originally held that vines will grow well in the very poorest of soil. Admittedly, poorer soils do grow grapes of a better quality than the strong rich soils, which are apt to sacrifice quality for quantity, but the vine will barely grow at all, let alone produce a grape, on an impoverished site, so some encouragement is vitally necessary if the aim is to produce some fruit. We are situated on the northernmost boundary of the grape producing countries, and if we cannot provide these plants with the longer summer and autumn growing season, greater number of sunshine hours per season, and the warmer climate of the Continent, we must take extra care of our vines in consequence and attend to their every whim if we desire success. A careful watch on behaviour and progress is the answer whatever the soil, be it rich or poor, then immediate steps can be taken to correct faults and safeguard the crop for the current year and for the years to come.

Rocky and shaly soils

Rocky and shaly soils are usually very poor, but remember that the Rhine and Moselle vineyards are entirely planted on steep shale slopes, and produce wine of undisputed internationally accepted quality. Once a vine has established itself and has sent its roots down deep, it will grow in such a site happily. Once again natural nourishment here is non-existent, and for anything like a crop much will have to be added in the form of plentiful supplies of manure and compost. Mulches added in the spring before growth begins, will both conserve moisture and assist growth. A vine naturally takes longer to establish itself and crop than those grown in more generous habitats, but given time and encouragement it will succeed. Akin to a sandy or gravel soil, rock and shale both hold and reflect the heat from the sun up to the wood and fruit of the vine which assists ripening quite considerably.

After reading this section it will be realised that all soils, even those not initially suitable, can be adapted to accommodate vines successfully and productively provided one is prepared to spend some time and hard work tilling and preparing the ground both before planting and during the occupation.

Planting the vine

Before planting, the vineyard should be marked out into rows running parallel from north to south so that each vine has the best of the sun by day. The distance between the rows of vines will be decided by the means by which the ground between these rows shall be cultivated. If the tilling and hoeing is to be done by hand, then the rows may be as close as 2′ 6″ to 5′ apart; but if a cultivator or a tractor is to be used then this is the width which must rule the spacing. Think ahead to the time when the vines are in full production, and if the vineyard is of such a size that a tractor-drawn trailer will be required to convey the crop to the press-house, and also for carrying manure on to the vineyard, bear this width in mind.

The spacing of the vines one from another down the rows is to a certain extent dictated by the soil itself; if it be poor then the vines may be as close as 2′ 6″ apart, but if it be rich then 4′–5′ spacing is recommended.

Whether the vines are to be planted against a wall or in an open vineyard site, the preparation and planting methods are the same.

The planting season extends from October through to March; October, November and March being the three best months for the task. There is little to choose between an autumn or a spring planting—if one plants in the autumn the vine will have had a good chance to develop the root system and gain a good hold before spring which means a much better start and growth rate during the first spring and summer. In a heavy, cold clay soil in an extremely wet and cold winter however, a vine might become very waterlogged and could perish if the roots rotted. This is less likely if plenty of drainage material is placed under the vines, but it is a possibility.

When planting a vine the best plan to follow is to provide the plant with all it will require for a year or two in the way of drainage and nourishment at the time of planting. This will save time and disappointment at a time when one will be fully occupied with other all important tasks, staking, wiring, training and pruning, all of which have to be done before the vine is two years old.

Take out a hole of approximately 12″ deep by 12″ square, piling the removed topsoil and subsoil separately. Line the bottom of the hole with *old* lime mortar, brick and tile rubble, and broken or ground bones, all of which provide an adequate drainage layer to prevent the vine becoming waterlogged. This material can be obtained from a builder when a building is being demolished, but be careful not to use any fresh cement mortar, which will burn the young roots. Cover this layer with either well rotted stable or farm-yard manure or compost to provide the young vines with nourishment during the early years of their development. Next fill in with the topsoil, planting the vine carefully into this medium spreading the roots out gently around the stem. Topsoil is a kinder and more generous environment into which to plant tender young roots than the harsher, often coarse, acid subsoil—hence the reason for piling them separately when digging the holes. Tread the vines in very well as the soil is filled in, then fill in the hole with the remaining subsoil and firm the soil again.

Diagram 2.

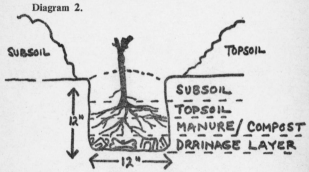

Preparation of the hole and planting the vine.

To plant a vine properly as explained will provide the very best possible beginning, and one should enjoy 100% success. It may be thought at this juncture that to take all this trouble just to plant a vine is a veritable waste of time . . . this is most certainly not so, for to follow this programme which can more easily be understood with the help of these two diagrams, will mean that your vines will both start away earlier in the spring, make better growth in their first and second year, and in consequence begin to crop earlier and more heavily than the vine that has just been pushed into a rough cleft pulled out by a spade.

Mark out the site with rows running north to south, next marking the positions of the prospective holes along these rows with canes, and then take out all the holes with a sharp spade. Follow this operation with barrows of rubble, spading some into each hole along the rows. Next take a barrow of the manure or compost down the rows, forking some into each hole firmly as you progress. Lastly, armed with the young vines, work your way once again down all the rows, planting a vine in each hole and filling them in firstly with the topsoil followed by the subsoil. Firm, well trodden vines will quickly establish themselves and be able to withstand the rigours of the wind and rain as the canes issue forth from the stems as season follows season.

If the vines are grafted they will have a waxed or calloused bulge about halfway up their main stem, and this scar must be covered with sifted soil or ashes after planting until the warmer weather, when it must be removed, to prevent the graft being rocked and loosened by the wind and weather. This advice ideally applies to all autumn planted vines, whether they be grafted or not, and it is a worthwhile practice to follow throughout the life of all outdoor vines, especially those that are grafted varieties.

In a situation where the chosen site is on a steep south or south-westerly slope, it is easier to terrace the ground and to plant the vines around the hill rather than having the rows running from top to bottom. For this there are two obvious reasons; firstly the ground is less likely to erode, and secondly the vines are more easily tended during cultivation, pruning and training. Due to the steepness of the hill the vines will be more exposed to the sun and air which is their life blood.

Diagram 3.

When planting vines down a steep slope plant them vertically to the horizontal of the line of the surface of the hill.

When planting on a steep incline remember to dig the holes and plant the vines at right angles to the slope as shown in the accompanying sketch, otherwise the roots will be too close to the surface and would be eroded and dried out too easily, and in consequence would blow loose from the soil, and thus die.

CHAPTER 4

Training and pruning

VINES planted in the open will in due course need substantial support as they grow, mature, and begin to fruit. The complete framework of supporting posts, wires and canes can be erected before or immediately after planting out the vines, but this task is not necessary until the vines enter their second year. There is plenty of work involved in the ground preparation and planting operations initially, and to provide a fairly stout cane to mark the positions of each vine, to which each vine may be tied as it grows in the first year is sufficient. Postponing the erection of posts and wire for a further season does spread the expense over two years, and this is quite a consideration in the case of the large vineyard venture.

Post and wire support

Metal or wooden posts may be used to support the vines. It is false economy to buy the cheapest materials initially for they have to be replaced so soon; always use the best you can acquire and they will last well. Oak or chestnut posts are naturally preferable to all other woods due to their longevity, larch and pine will last about seven years, ash and silver birch and other soft woods are useless in the ground and will rot off in a year.

At either end of each row of vines a really strong post is recommended; this must be inserted deeply into the ground, if the vineyard is of some considerable size then an equally strong post will be required at intervals of every fifth vine along the rows. Intermediate posts can be of lesser wood or metal, or even strong eight foot canes can be used, but these are apt to become loose in the soil and blow out. The two end posts will require a support to keep them strained apart and the wires really taut.

The lowest wire which eventually takes the weight of the fruiting cane should be gauge 12, and should be run some 18″ above ground level. At 12″ above this wire run a double wire from end to end, and near the top of the posts run yet another double wire which acts as a stabiliser for the framework as a whole, using wire of gauge 14 for all other than the bottom row. Tie or staple the wires to each cane or stake along the rows so that they do not sag with the weight of the vines, for when the vines begin to crop and are fully foliaged they provide resistance to a gale force wind akin to that of a ship under full sail which soon floors all but the most substantial support systems. You have been warned!

Diagram 4.

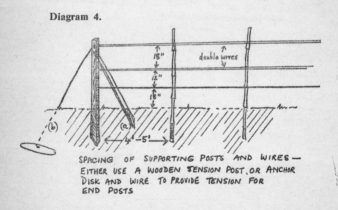

SPACING OF SUPPORTING POSTS AND WIRES— EITHER USE A WOODEN TENSION POST, OR ANCHOR DISK AND WIRE TO PROVIDE TENSION FOR END POSTS

The system of support for vines that has been recommended illustrates the so called "Guyot" method of training and pruning, innovated by Dr. Jules Guyot in about 1850 which will be explained in full shortly.

Spacing

A poor soil will not produce such a growth of cane as would be produced by a vine in a richer soil, and this factor should govern the distance between vines. No larger crop per acre is produced from a longer cane run per vine, but if a vine planted in rich soil were planted at a distance of 2′ 6″ apart it would produce an embarrassing amount of un-wanted sappy growth, whereas planted at 5′ apart the growth/cropping ratio is balanced. Conversely, a vine grown in poor chalk soil and given a 5′ run would not be able to furnish the distance with sufficient foliage and fruit to merit the space allowed; whereas given a 3′ stretch it would be able to work at optimum productivity on such a soil.

Vine training and pruning

Vines, whether grafted or rooted cuttings, will have been planted sometime between October and March into their permanent new home, and must at once be cut right down hard to leave only three or four good buds. This will force all the great surge of energy that is generated into all plants in the spring into these remaining buds, and in April or May these same buds will burst and the young shoots will emerge.

After a week or so it will become evident that one or two shoots are stronger and tougher than others. Rub off all but the two strongest shoots which will carry all the growth of the vine in the current year. When it becomes evident which is the stronger cane, pinch off the weaker leaving a stub of some three inches only, this provides one with a basis for new cane should an accident befall the master cane, and for replacement wood for the following season.

It is more straightforward both to explain and to follow the principles of training and pruning with the aid of diagrams. Therefore, we now follow the progress of two young newly planted vines, outwardly identical, but differing in perfor-mance, representing any two vines in an embryo vineyard.

If possible it is beneficial to remove all lateral growth issuing from the leaf axils, for this growth merely saps the

Diagram 5.

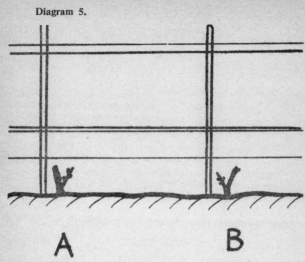

Vines A and B at planting time.

Diagram 6.

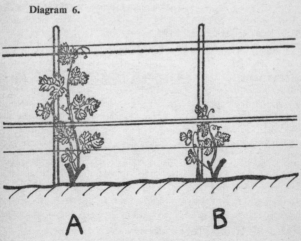

Vines A and B in following September.

strength and slows the ripening of the main canes. It also deprives the growth and fruiting buds of the following year which are forming in the leaf axils of essential nourishment. These shoots are nipped off between finger and thumb at an inch from the main cane to avoid damaging the dormant bud in the leaf axil.

As the young vine grows it must be tied in at intervals to its cane to prevent its flopping and being snapped off by the wind.

By September Vine A has grown very much better than its neighbour, Vine B; this fact does not matter for during the first year the main aim is to build up a good deep widespread root system for each vine, a process much aided by the careful ground preparation immediately prior to planting, and the preparation of the hole itself. A vine may make as little as six inches or as much as five or six feet during the first year.

In the following January all vines must be once again pruned back to leave just three or four buds as before at the

Diagram 7.

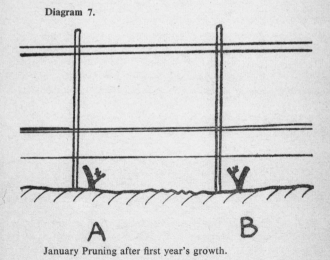

January Pruning after first year's growth.

bottom of the two canes as here illustrated. This operation must be carried out for the long-term good of the vine, for if it were allowed to crop in this, its second year, this would so undermine the strength of the vine that it would fail to crop in the following season, and possibly for many seasons. A vine must establish a good root system in order to crop to the maximum of its ability.

A vine is a plant that should have a long life ahead of it, and to sap its powers seriously before it is mature enough to produce will probably damage its performance for some time, if not for ever. Patience is a virtue at this stage!

Outdoor vines are pruned in January because it is at this time that all the sap, the life blood of the plant, has receded into the roots for the winter, leaving the vines completely dormant. This is therefore the only safe period in which mature ripe wood and canes may be pruned. Mid-February is the latest vines should be pruned, for in a mild winter the sap will very soon be on the move, especially in southern counties. Pruning late in a precocious spring can result in the sap bleeding extensively, a horrifying sight that need never happen.

The vines are now entering their second season, when the majority of them will be creating cane to provide fruit in the third year; so now is the time to put in the posts and wires if this has not been done earlier. Again, tie in the young canes as they grow, and remove all lateral growth as it puts in an appearance; this may not be practicable on a commercial scale.

To return once more to the progress of Vine A and Vine B; the former has grown most satisfactorily and by September has topped its supporting cane with a strong ripe pencil-thick cane, whereas Vine B has again failed to emulate this example. This is nothing to worry about; Vine B is merely taking more time to produce an adequate root system and all its energy is being devoted to this rather than to making top growth. To put this early phase into perspective, a plant which has an expected productive life ahead of between 20 to 50 years, or perhaps more can afford to take a little longer over adolescence! On average about ninety per cent. of the newly planted vines in a vineyard follow the example of Vine A planted in a well balanced soil, though if the soil is very poor a quarter will take the extra year to mature. The slow vines

Diagram 8.

A   B

September growth at the end of second season.

Diagram 9.

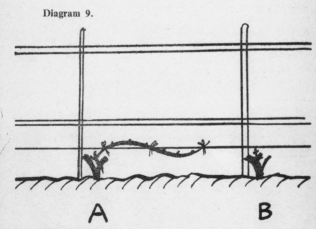

A   B

January pruning at the beginning of the third season.
Vine A to crop for the first time.

will catch up their more forward companions and by the time the vines have reached their fifth year there will be no difference in appearance or performance.

January, the pruning month, comes round again, and the stronger of the two canes produced by Vine A in the previous season is chosen to carry the first crop, and is gently persuaded down and tied firmly along the bottom wire. Most canes have an unripe tip, and this must be cut away or it will attract mildew.

Trim the cane to fit the run of wire allowed per vine. The lesser cane is cut away, but remember to leave a stub having two or three buds to provide fresh long replacement canes for the year ahead.

With Vine B all new growth is pruned away leaving just three or four buds on one of the stubs to supply canes for the oncoming season of growth. This severe treatment will inspire extra vigour for the future and as a result should produce sufficient ripened wood to crop in the following year.

Care of fruiting vines

With Spring the buds which have formed at approximately 6″ intervals along the horizontal fruiting cane will swell and burst and begin to grow upwards at an amazing pace.

Disbudding

If all the shoots sprouting from these canes were allowed to develop, there would be such a forest of growth that any hope of control would be useless. Therefore, a programme of selection has to be practised to leave just one shoot per 6–9″ according to whether the cane is 3′ or 5′ in length. Do not be in too great a hurry to carry out the thinning; wait until each shoot shows the presence of minute bunches, and then choose the strongest and best endowed shoot at the pre-arranged intervals, and then carefully pinch off all others. By waiting for the fruiting shoots to identify themselves, the disappointment of being left with barren shoots is avoided.

In this, the first season of fruition, no more than one bunch per lateral may be kept or the stamina of the vine will be severely undermined. If there is more than one embryo bunch on each lateral, wait until the best one can be identified before eliminating the remainder. As the vine grows older, it may be allowed gradually to carry more fruit, no more than four or five bunches in the first year, seven or eight in the second, a dozen or so in the third fruiting season, and when the vine is approaching its prime in the fifth year it may be allowed to carry as many as it throws, within reason. If a phenomenal crop is thrown, and one succumbs to the temptation to allow such a crop to ripen, this will probably so undermine the stamina of the vine that it will die in time. Heavy crops must not be borne until the fifth year or after. Remember, never allow a crop to be excessive.

Do not, however, postpone this disbudding operation too late, or the vine will bleed profusely if the shoots have reached a fair size; keep a careful watch for differing varieties begin to shoot at different times.

One point to watch is that the hybrid vine Seyve-Villard 5/276, has an annoying habit peculiar to itself, a habit which can sometimes cost the entire crop. It throws up the embryonic flower shoots at the top of the new growth which means that these flowers are more vulnerable to frost damage than other varieties which keep their flowers well hidden as long as possible.

Flowering

As the laterals grow, tuck them first between the lower, then the upper parallel double wires. Once well through the higher, shear the growing tips off thus reverting and concentrating the energy force into flowering and grape production. The greater the leaf area above the fruit, the higher the eventual sugar content. The leaves are the sugar factories.

In fine weather wind and insects attend to the pollination, the latter attracted by the delicate scent of vine flowers, but it never comes amiss to give each vine a gentle kick, or to run the flowers gently though your hand one after the other to make sure the task is done efficiently, especially in a poor year. In dull wet weather the flowers cannot pollinate naturally so easily, and at such times hand pollination on a dry day after the caps of the flowers have been ejected will assist no end. The pollination period drags out painfully at such times and this is the major cause of a poor or non-existent crop.

Diagram 10.

Flowers of the vine.

Control of sub-lateral growth ... summer pruning

After the tips of the fruiting laterals have been pinched out, sub-lateral growth will be greatly stimulated. If time allows these shoots should be pinched out immediately after the first leaf. All possible energy must be devoted to the production of fruit, and all sub-lateral growth contributes nothing to the good of the vine or the grapes. The task of nourishing the vine and ripening the crop is undertaken by the larger leaves produced on lateral canes which must not be removed. Also keep a check on the sub-lateral material thrown by the replacement canes, and pinch these out as they appear at about an inch from the main cane.

This control of unwanted shoots is a continuous chore throughout the summer months, and if neglected the vine will become a tangled mass of foliage and be a great attraction to mildew due to lack of air circulation. In addition a preventative rather than a curative spraying programme geared to a wet or dry summer to prevent mildews and other troubles, weeding and correcting any soil deficiencies are the tasks that must be attended to all summer until the vines are due to be cropped, and are dealt with in future sections of this book.

Vine A has now cropped successfully for the first time, and the slower Vine B has grown sufficient wood to be able to bear fruit in the new year. To show clearly how these two vines appear refer to the diagram.

Diagram 11.

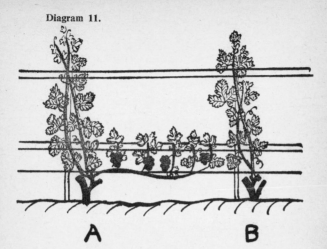

A   B

State of vines A and B in third September; vine A
bearing four bunches, vine B has at last grown well.

January pruning

Vine A has the rod that has recently fruited cut right
away, and the stronger of the two replacement canes, after
trimming to fit the length of wire, is tied down on to the bottom
wire to crop in the current season. Remember to leave two
buds on the stub of the removed lesser replacement cane to
supply two new such replacements during the new growing
season.

With Vine B the better of the two canes is trimmed and
tied down on to the lowest wire to fruit; again, leave the two
buds on the stub of the cane that is removed to supply new
replacements in due course.

This completes the explanation on the Guyot system of
training and pruning a grape vine; if a weakling vine should
yet again fail to make enough wood in the third year to
begin to fruit, be harsh and cut again hard to the stem, leaving
the two or three buds for new growth. It will catch up eventually providing no rot or other trouble has attacked the roots.

A modification on the Guyot system, known as double
Guyot, is shown in this diagram—which though producing

Diagram 12.

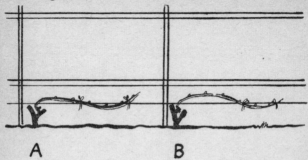

A   B

Vines A and B at the beginning of the fourth season
both having been tied down to fruit after the January
pruning session.

Diagram 13.

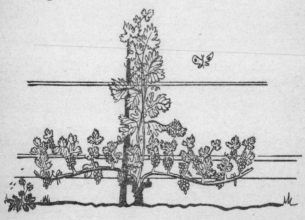

A double-Guyot trained vine ripening a good crop of
grapes . . . September/November.

no more fruit per vine, is perhaps an easier and less cumbersome method for a fully laden and generous vine. This system has gained a greater following of late than single Guyot due to the fact that many vines crop more heavily on cane nearer the stem or trunk of the vine; an important factor.

Diagram 14.

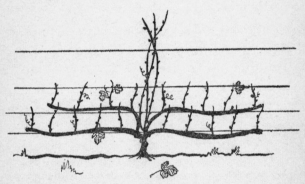

A double-double Guyot trained vine shown after cropping and leaf fall; note three or four replacement canes; suitable for MADELEINE-ANGEVINE, BACO I, TRIOMPHE D'ALSACE.

Semi-permanent cordon training

Baco I is the most vigorous vine of all, and the only method of taming and cropping this vine in the open vineyard, unless it is on chalk soil which naturally is a great check to rampant tendencies, is to use a semi-permanent method of training. Here there are three canes tiered horizontally on each side of the main stem. Two or more of these canes can be replaced each January. The lateral fruiting canes which sprout from these canes are spur-pruned to leave just two buds on each spur each January.

Diagram 15.

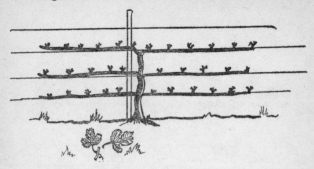

A semi-permanent cordon trained vine showing pruned spurs cut back to two buds; suitable for BACO I especially.

Goblet pruning

The greater majority of British viticulturists use the Guyot method for the open vineyard, but there is an alternative method of training known as Goblet pruning which is a system which has small but growing following here. These two methods are those used in the vineyards of Europe and have over many many years been found to be the most successful in that the vigour of the vine is severely checked annually and in this manner will produce a worthwhile crop. The goblet system shapes the vine into a bush.

With Goblet pruning the treatment in the first year is similar to that practised in Guyot pruning; grow a cane from the stem and tie it on to a stout 5' stake as growth proceeds. In January cut the cane well down leaving two buds for the new year's growth. In the second season follow the same principle again, growing a single upright cane from each vine and allowing all lateral and top growth to remain, thus encouraging the stem to thicken and strengthen. In the following January cut the vine down to a height of about 18". In the ensuing season growth is allowed only from the top three buds, the remainder being rubbed off as they appear. These three laterals are tied on to the stake as they grow, and may

Diagram 16—Goblet Pruning.

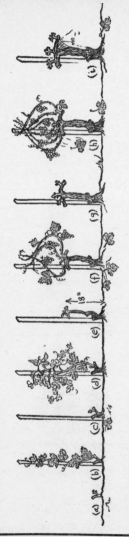

(a) Newly planted vine; (b) First season's growth; (c) After January pruning; (d) Second season's growth in September; (e) January pruning showing 18" stem or leg; (f) Showing three fruiting canes in third season; (g) January pruning leaving two buds on each spur for following season's growth; (h) In the fourth year there are six fruiting canes each with just *one* bunch of grapes; (i) January pruning again; prune each cane to two buds, but allow only six fruiting laterals in the following and ensuing seasons or the vines will be overtaxed.

fruit, but only one or two bunches may be kept or the stamina and future of the vine will be seriously jeopardized.

Next January these three laterals are pruned to leave two buds on the stump of each, which will in time produce six new lateral canes which will throw many bunches of fruit; these must again be reduced to a total according to the vigour of the vine from six to eight bunches. Pinch the tips of these growing canes out some eight or ten leaves beyond the last flower shoot when the vines are in flower to encourage a good set, and loosely tie the canes in above to the stake when they are long and tough enough so that they sag naturally. Keep all sub-lateral growth pinched out, and do not allow any more canes other than the chosen six to develop. When January comes round again, each of the six canes are once again shortened to two buds each, giving a total of twelve buds for the following year. Twelve shoots would be too many to control, so the strongest six or eight shoots issuing from these spurs or stubs are kept, and the remainder are rubbed off.

This is the annual pattern to follow throughout the life of a Goblet pruned vine which is a form of spur pruning; having all growth centred around the one stake obviously there is a limit to the number of laterals, which should never number more than six to nine on each vine. Keep all sub-lateral growth severely pinched out, and do not allow the vine to crop heavily until the fifth or sixth year. In the event of an enormous crop being thrown, if this were allowed to ripen the future of the vine would be threatened, so check on the number of bunches borne on each vine. This will vary according to the vigour of the different varieties.

This system does not suit all varieties of vine, in particular neither those varieties possessed of very thin frail cane nor those of tremendous vigour. Some types of vine are inclined to throw fruit at the furthest rather than the nearer end of the cane; these three types of vine are better trained according to Dr. Jules Guyot.

These rigid training methods are the product of many centuries of trial and error, and it is desirable to follow them because in this country we are on the outer perimeter of the vine producing area (the emphasis here is on the word "producing," for vines will grow anywhere in the northern hemisphere). There is a limit to the northern latitude where a vine will both happily produce and, more important, ripen its crop regularly and successfully. The Guyot method, bearing its crop little more than a foot from the ground, takes advantage of heat radiation from the ground, and is therefore the system that might be used in the borderline sites in this country. It is also the easiest method of training due to the fact that support is supplied for all possible growth at all times which keeps the canes and laterals clean and away from the ground, and less liable to storm damage, quite a point in its favour.

Multi-cane and single loop pruning

Multi-cane pruning and single loop pruning is of interest where the vineyard is on a very steep slope, and the use of wire trellis is completely out of the question. The former system is widely used on the steep Moselle hillsides, the latter also, but to a lesser degree. The vines would be planted at either $4' \times 4'$ or $5' \times 5'$ stations to allow a very free air circulation, and each given a tall slim stake for support. The canes are annually replaced by young wood, the principles here being similar to the Guyot system in this respect, but in common with the Goblet pruning methods, weed control is made easier by virtue of cross cultivation due to the absence of wires.

The Lenz Moser system

This method, fairly recently widely publicised by Dr. Lenz Moser, an Austrian, is designed to save time and labour, and to avoid endless back-breaking bending by presenting the working area of the vine at face level. This is a revolutionary improvement, but whether the absence of heat reflection from the ground, more particularly as the grapes approach ripeness, will result in a poorer ripening of both the fruit and the replacement wood, and a greater tendency towards mildew remains to be seen. Either spur or cane replacement pruning may be practised here.

Diagram 17.

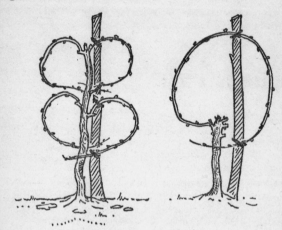

Multi-cane cane Pruning —
widely used in Moselle

Single loop cane pruning —
also used in Moselle

Diagram 18.

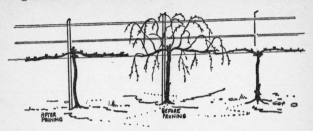

Lenz Moser system — vines 5′ 10′ apart; rows 10′ apart.
Spur or cane pruning may be used.

Geneva double curtain

This method follows the principles of Dr. Lenz Moser by training the vines high, but here each vine is trained outwards from the main stem to run along parallel wires which are held in place by wooden stretchers fixed to the top of each upright. Rows are from 9′–10′ apart, and the vines from 5′–10′ apart from one another along the rows.

Either cane or spur pruming may be practised here. Both the Lenz Moser and Geneva Double Curtain systems are relatively new in England at the time of writing, and to date no vineyard using either is sufficiently mature to have produced a crop of grapes. Therefore no recommendations can be made as to the virtue or otherwise of either method.

Diagram 19.

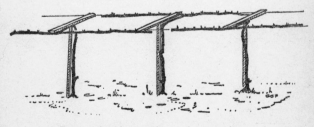

Geneva double curtain — after pruning —
spur or cane pruning may be used.

High tensile trellis

Recently some vinegrowers have been using high tensile wire to support their vines, and due to the very considerable degree of tension achieved using this wire, few if any intermediate posts are needed along rows of great length. This wire is stretched between the two large endposts, usually ex-railway sleepers or telegraph poles, correct spacing of the wires is maintained with metal droppers.

High tensile trellis is particularly suitable for the Lenz Moser system of training vines; others use a strand of high tensile wire, which can be stretched, for the bottom wire with Guyot trained vines with considerable success.

Great care must be excercised however in the use of this wire, for should it become un-moored at one end, it could do considerable damage to a leg, arm or even neck should one be in the way of the released wire.

CHAPTER 5

Manuring

BEFORE planting up a vineyard of any size it is advisable to enlist the help of your county Horticultural Advisory Officer and have a soil sample taken. From this test he will be able to ascertain whether the soil is well balanced or deficient in certain elements. If deficient it is, you will be expertly advised on ways and means to correct the soil balance, whether the soil is in need of lime, and so on.

Many believe, and rightly so, that the vine will grow and crop on the poorest soil, in ground which due to its extreme poverty is not suitable for any plant other than the vine. This is true; a vine can be grown on land too steep for any other plant, too dry, stony and exposed, but vines, occupying the same land for many years as they do, establish themselves due to their habit of extremely deep roots which they send far down into the sub-strata in their search for sustenance.

But given no nourishment the yield from such vines will be very poor, the growth will be miserable, for we cannot in this country supply hot sunshine, indeed many months of hot sunshine that is to be found in more southerly locations on the Continent to compensate for such mean conditions, our growing season is just too short.

So we have to compromise. The early pioneers of the new British viticulture who originally advocated complete starvation are now recommending a regular programme of feeding for the vineyard, and in fact follow this out with their own vines. A certain degree of vigour is required to keep the vines productive, thus they will produce a worthwhile crop. No hard and fast rule can be laid down, for no two sites are similar, and every vinegrower must discover the perfect balance for his own plantation for himself.

It may be argued here that all we take annually from a vine is a mere pound or so of grapes, but reflect just how much wood is pruned away each winter, wood that the vine has produced in just one year, all the leaves that have been produced and have blown away at leaf fall, and all the unwanted shoots that are pinched out during the growing season. This all represents a considerable amount of lost energy from one small plant in one year. We cannot take without giving back, or the vine will become poorer and poorer as it extracts all the available nutrients from the soil, and cropping will eventually cease.

Foliar feeding

A very effective method of feeding vines is by the use of organic foliar feed, especially useful during the growing season when perhaps a lack of vigour is noted, or certain deficiencies come to light. Being a balanced feed, and applied through the leaves of the vine, the food factories of the plant, the effect is instantaneous. Almost immediately one notices a darkening of leaf colour, increased vigour, and a higher sugar content in the grapes, the latter alone being reason enough. If the ph of your soil is above 7.0, use the foliar feed with added iron. Recommended rate of use is fortnightly, applied only during dull weather, or after sundown, otherwise the leaves could scorch. A further point worthy of mention, the foliar feed "Maxicrop" may be used in conjunction with copper and sulphur sprays upon which it works as a catalyst; one can then feed and apply mildew preventatives at one and the same time, instead of in three separate spraying operations.

Preparation prior to planting

Some advice has been given in chapter 3 on this problem; a point worth noting is that for the larger planting, county level advice is invaluable when the success and output of a commercial venture is at stake.

This soil analysis may show the soil to be deficient in one or more of the three basic elements, namely, nitrogen, potash and phosphates. Nitrogen can be best supplied by digging in organic material such as compost or preferably animal manures which gradually release their components into the soil thus supplying their beneficial effects over a long period. One has to be careful when supplying natural or artificial nitrogenous manures that the application be necessary, and that the amount is not too great at any one time or the total result will be masses of sappy cane growth and masses of leaf at the expense of fruit.

Potash and phosphates contribute much towards the production of fruit assisting the sugar content, and thus ultimately the alcohol content of the wine. Here again, unless there is a marked deficiency in either, no more than ½ cwt. of each per acre is required per annum.

A pH test will reveal whether or not the soil is lime deficient, a pH lower than 6.5 requires a dressing of lime, which should not be added during the same autumn as manure, but may be applied during the following spring. The balance of lime additon is very delicate indeed, too much leads to chlorosis in certain varieties which has to be corrected with organic manures and/or salts of iron. On the other hand in a lime deficient soil, lime helps to break up the manires into humus, also it breaks up the molecules of a heavy clay soil, encouraging a more crumbly friable soil, and assisting soil bacterial action. Certain varieties of vine grow well and crop satisfactorily on chalk or limestone soils, namely, Seyve-Villard 5/276 and Baco 1.

One point to bear in mind here is that if only one element is lacking, other elements cannot be assimilated by a vine or any other plant in its absence, therefore one has to add all three providing the deficient element in the greater quantity to attempt to rectify the imbalance.

Magnesium deficiency may be suspected when a chloritic condition of the leaves occurs (if it is certain that there is not an excess of lime in the soil). This can be identified by the leaves taking on a yellowish look often with burnt looking edges to the leaves and can be rectified by applying magnesium sulphate in the form of Epsom Salts in very small amounts. The presence of magnesium enables the lime to go about its work; it is not often that there is a lack of magnesium in the soil, but when chloritic conditions rear their heads either through there being an excess of lime or a magnesium deficiency, a dose of Epsom Salts is the answer!

To sum up: if the site is very poor and deficient in humus, a light dressing of organic manure should be dug in prior to planting in the autumn. This will also take care of the nitrogen supply. If there be a marked lack of potash or phosphate apply this in April or May, or they will have been leached away before the young vines have enough root to be able to take advantage of their presence.

Annual assessment of progress

As time goes by keep a close watch on the progress and performance of the vines, on the rate of cane growth, on leaf size and colour, and ultimately on whether enough flower shoots are being thrown, for if vines are grown in a suitable medium they will be healthy and more disease resistant; a vine will soon tell the observant viticulturist if any adjustment is necessary.

Too high a nitrogen content will make itself evident by excessive growth, large rich dark green leaves, thick cane, and ultimate loss in productivity, whereas nitrogen deficiency makes itself clear by the very opposite, a lack of enthusiasm, slow growth, poor leaf colour, and a lack of flower shoots. In general apply organic manures, which must be well rotted, in the autumn so they become thoroughly assimilated by spring.

In general it is safe to apply a light dressing of potash and phosphates every other spring, wood ashes spread around the vines in spring are very beneficial, especially after an extremely wet year when most, if not all, these elements are leached away. After producing a bumper crop, too, the vines will appreciate a boost application. Superphosphate and sulphate of potash are the best forms.

Take an annual pH reading to see if lime is necessary, if the results are positive, do not add the lime at the same time as the organic manure application, but apply it during the following spring. Lime is a great releaser of other elements into the soil quite apart from the sweetening effect it has on sour, acid stagnant soils; it also encourages clay to break up and gradually to become more manageable.

CHAPTER 6

Vine disorders and their prevention

VINES maintained in a healthy condition are far less likely to contact disease or attract insect pests; the soil balance, resulting in healthy vigorous virile vines is the greatest deterrent. The weather is the unpredictable factor, for a wet, humid year encourages mildew to develop and spread, and we have in every 10 years in general one really superb year and one good year; the remaining eight years range from fair to frankly abominable! Therefore it is no good leaving mildew to chance, hoping that it will not come your way, for it has the awkward habit of establishing itself and multiplying in the breathing holes or stomata underneath the leaves as mycelium for some two weeks prior to becoming visible to the naked eye. If one attempts curative action, often the mildew has gone too far to be effectively checked. Therefore a simple spraying programme has been evolved, geared to whether the year is dry or wet and humid, which it is recommended that all dedicated and conscientious vine growers should follow.

There are two main types of mildew, namely Oidium and Peranospera. The former is checked by sulphur, and the latter by copper fungicides, namely, Bordeaux mixture or powder, which can be applied wet or in powder form, or by using Zineb or Dithane as a spray.

Oidium, or powdery mildew
(*Uncinula Necator*)

This can be identified quite easily by appearance—it forms a fine grey powdery skin on the leaves, young canes and on the grapes themselves. It can attack the young spring shoots and thus destory the embryo bunches of grapes which shrivel and burn up. It can attack at any time during the growing season, but is most prevalent when the heat of summer subsides and the humid dampness of autumn follows, forming ideal conditions for mildew attack. Murphy's soluble sulphur is the most effective deterrent here, applied at the ratio of $6\frac{1}{2}$ oz. to 22 gallons of water, ($3\frac{1}{4}$ oz. in 11 gallons). In midsummer 10 gallons of spray will cover 100 vines, therefore one will require 200 gallons of spray for an acre of vines at each spraying. Where few vines are grown, they can be dusted with Boot's yellow sulphur and Bordeaux powder at a ratio of 1-2 which will guard the vines against both mildews. This may be applied with a puffer on a dull, damp day when the powder will readily adhere to the damp leaves and berries.

Peranospera, or downy mildew

(*Plasmopara Viticola*)

This mildew is identified by pale translucent spreading patches on the upper side of the vine leaves, and is of a more serious nature than Oidium. As the mildew develops a thick white down forms on the underside of the leaf, and indeed the grapes themselves may be affected by the white down. If this mildew strikes late in the season the berries turn a dull brown colour and refuse to ripen, retaining an intense acidity. It is not common at this late stage, but in a poor sunless season when grapes are particularly slow to ripen, this softening and browning can occur, in particular to the black vine variety, Seibel 5455. Here Murphy's Zineb or P.B.I. Dithane may be used at a ratio of 10 oz. in 22 gallons, (5 oz. to 11 gallons, $2\frac{1}{2}$ oz. to $5\frac{1}{2}$ gallons). Please refer to amounts needed for 100 vines or an acre of vines above.

This mildew, in common with anthracnose, forms within the breathing spores of the leaf in the presence of droplets of water, and multiplies rapidly, sending out zoospores which search around to find a new breathing spore into which they insert themselves and thus continue the cycle. Once the mildew has introduced itself into the leaf, the fungicide is unable to make any impression, and can only prevent further infection. Two weeks only are needed for a considerable infection to build up before it becomes visible to the human eye, hence the need for a regular spraying programme to prevent trouble rather than attempt a cure.

Anthracnose, or black spot

Akin to the other mildews, anthracnose is more prevalent in warm, wet, damp weather, and though comparatively uncommon, this trouble is more likely when other plants in the area carry this disease year after year. Sycamore trees and roses can be the culprits in this case, and a wet year will see more overwintering spores deposited ready to attack in the following season.

This is identified by black/brown spots on the cane itself, which can merge one into the other. After leaf fall, if these spots are found all prunings should be burnt.

Anthracnose is controlled by copper preparations which can be applied at a slightly stronger solution than for Peranospera.

Outdoor spraying programme

1st Spray in mid-April

Mix 10 oz. (300 grams) of Zineb with $6\frac{1}{2}$ oz. (200 grams) of soluble sulphur with a little water to a consistency of thick cream, and then add to 22 gallons of water. Maxicrop, a foliar feed made from seaweed, can be added to the spray at this stage as it acts as a catalyst and keeps the two chemicals in suspension, and aids the spray to adhere to the vine leaves. It has been proven in the Champagne area of France that Maxicrop produces riper wood and fruit, and also higher sugar content in the grapes.

It can be appreciated that one is able to take preventitive measures against both mildews with the one spray and feed the vines at the same time. At this particular stage it will be appreciated that the spray goes a very long way due to the small amount of leaf growth so early in the season.

2nd, 3rd, 4th, and 5th sprays

Spray the vines with the above mixture every two weeks until flowering, when all spraying must cease.

Post Blossom

Repeat the above spraying recipe of two to three week intervals according to the weather, adding 7 fl. oz. (200 cc) of Malathion if Red Spider or other insects or caterpillars are proving a problem. Wear protective clothing as this insecticide is very poisonous.

Early September

Once the berries approach 'veraison', the stage when white grapes begin to assume a yellow translucent colour and black grapes begin to darken, all spraying must cease.

Traubenspray, obtainable from A. E. Massel, (address at the rear of the book), or Elvaron should quickly be applied to those varieties which are prone to botrytis, mixing instructions on the packets. No further spray is necessary.

Seyve-villard and Coulure

Many vinegrowers have noticed that immediately prior to flowering, the vine Seyve-Villard 5/276 is frequently prone apt to a withering and browning of the flowers before they open, resulting in a total loss of crop. This only occurs in areas of neutral or acid soils, not with vines grown on chalk or limestone.

The answer here is an application of lime over the root area of each vine in late May, no earlier and no later; this practice to be repeated annually. A recommended dose would be a good shovel-full per vine, forked in to the soil gently and evenly, and "coulure", or flower dropping, and withering will be a thing of the past.

Pourriture noble, or the noble rottenness

This is a fungus which only develops in certain years and under certain conditions. It requires a balance of warmth and humidity in the autumn, and makes its appearance on the skin of the grapes as a grey powdery skin, which, if the grapes are sound, results in an evaporation of the water within the grape, and the sugar remains. The resulting wine has a truly noble character, Chateau D'Yquem and the German "Trockenbeerenauslese" wines being perhaps the most famous to be made from such grapes. These grapes have a withered shrivelled look, quite different from those affected by the grey rot, or Pourriture grise, which is caused by over-ripenness, wet weather, or punctured grapes, and rots the bunches.

So valuable is this noble rottenness to the vinegrowers of the Sauternes area that the vintage is spread over many weeks as the pickers *only* pick the affected bunches at each picking, and have to re-pick as many as eight times! This perhaps goes some way to explain the high prices asked for the best Sauternes.

This fungus is unusual in this country for it is rarely warm enough when the grapes are ripening in the autumn, it can however be induced under glass where humidity and warmth can be controlled somewhat, and if wine grapes are produced thus, superb wine can be made.

Insect pests

Sometimes aphids invade vines in the spring and summer, and according to variety they can usually be despatched by spreading Derris around the base of the vines, so that the insects, on descending to the ground at night, come into contact with the powder and thus perish. According to the variety of the pest, your local horticultural shop or chemist will advise on the latest and most efficient cure for the trouble. To state a product for each pest would be rash, for almost every month or so a new product is issued which supersedes the earlier preparation for one pest or another.

Diagram 20—Pests of the vine:

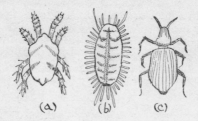

(a) Red Spider; (b) Mealy bug; (c) Vine Weevil.

Virus trouble

Though rare, this disease does sometimes appear, and is noticeable by the cane growth of the vine becoming distorted. The lengths of cane between the joints become shorter and grow off at different angles, healthy cane having a regular length of straight cane between each joint. Any vine so affected must be dug up and burnt immediately, as this trouble is very contagious to others either by insect or air contact. The results are serious; fruiting fails in time, and the vine reverts into a distorted bushy being.

Phylloxera

In about 1860 this pest was introduced into France from America (as were the mildews) and it commenced to ravage all but a handful of the thousands of the European vineyards, causing widespread ruin and horror in its path. This pest kills the vines, for at one time in its incredible and unique life history it takes up residence among the roots of the vine and feeds upon the smaller roots, thus rendering it immune from any human preventative action with sprays, etc. At an earlier stage this insect makes itself at home on the leaves where it creates galls wherein the larvae develop to emerge either as egg laying females or as hermaphrodites. The offspring form either into leaf sucking, or the more deadly root sucking variety of Phylloxera. The gall is the identifying feature.

Diagram 21.

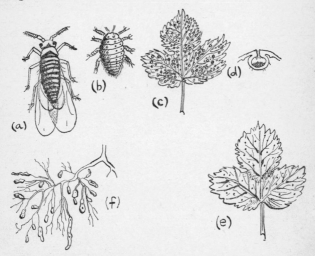

The life history of the Phylloxera vastatrix:

(a) A winged female; (b) a wingless female from the root; (c) Under-surface of the leaf showing the galls; (d) An enlarged section of one of the galls showing the eggs within; (e) Upper surface of an infected vine leaf showing the gall openings; (f) Some vine roots showing the nodosites caused by the parasite.

This pest is not at present resident in Great Britain, though there have been two recent outbreaks resulting from importing infected rooted vines from the Continent. This practice is to be deplored as it puts all the English vineyards at risk; it is quite safe to import un-rooted cuttings, however.

All the French and other Continental vineyards had to be replanted entirely with their own vines grafted on to American rootstocks, a vast undertaking, for the extreme vigour of the American roots merely causes more roots to develop if the Phylloxera attacks instead of expiring like the sparser and weaker rooted European vine. Also a range of Euro-American hybrid vines have been evolved incorporating the vigour of one and the quality of the other; these are to a great extent mildew and disease resistant.

It is much safer to use grafted vines if a large vineyard of several acres is planned, in case Phylloxera were to become endemic here. The resultant wine is not of such high quality as that from an ungrafted vine; it is quicker maturing, and the yield per vine is somewhat lower; this is very evident when a grafted and an ungrafted vine of the same variety are planted side by side.

To conclude, do not let all this worry you; mildew is the only threat we have to contend with in general, and this does not necessarily attack every year. Providing the vines are healthy in themselves, and the sulphur and copper spraying or dusting programme is adhered to, all should be well—the other troubles being a rare occurrence.

Mildew preventatives

There are several branded chemical products on the market for the specific control of mildew, Zineb and Benlate being two that come to mind. Though obviously efficient, one must appreciate that some chemicals, Bordeaux mixture included, tend to delay ripening by several days for each application. Mildew deterrents are nevertheless essential, particularly where grapes are being produced commercially, but it does pay to look into all benefits and drawbacks of these products before use.

With the long overdue and very essential concern over the protection of our environment, and bearing in mind that the end product is to be drunk by mankind, do take especial care to discover that any fungicide, insecticide and weed-killer used is safe for the user and for wild life and cannot remain for ever locked in the soil or water systems.

CHAPTER 7

Cropping the vines

AS the grapes begin to ripen they attract the unwelcome attention of the wasps and the birds, particularly blackbirds. It is pointless to go to all the trouble to purchase, plant and train vines over a period of several years simply for the benefit of these voracious pests, so some protection must be provided. They will devour the grapes well before they are either ripe enough for eating or for making into wine, and it is useless to think that you can beat the birds and wasps to the grapes and avoid protective measures.

Wasps

The threat of wasp damage can be overcome with sensible forethought and planning. When the plums begin to ripen, this heralds the arrival of the wasps *en masse*; try to locate nests by keeping a watch around the banks and hedges in the evenings when these pests will be returning home. Nests can be eradicated by one of several methods, some will recommend pouring paraffin down the hole, others recommend boiling water, a puffer of insecticide should also quell all activity successfully; I believe that one can use cyanide but it is extremely dangerous material if there is any likelihood of any other animals coming into contact. A chemist or garden shop would most likely advise the best method for each particular nest.

Secondly, if wasps are being troublesome, wasp traps can be set up at intervals around the vineyard. Smear jampots with jam or honey inside, and half fill them with water, cider, beer or wine, and set them into the ground firmly and they should go a long way in competing successfully with the unripe grapes.

Thirdly, if vines are being grown on a large scale it is a wise plan to choose varieties of vine that ripen in October or November after the wasps have disappeared to hibernate for the winter. Obviously such vine types would vary from area to area; perhaps a careful study of chapter 1 would be of assistance here. In the Midlands and northern districts of the country this problem will not arise for only the very earliest varieties ripen there in any case. In the southern half of the country where there is a wide range of varieties suitable for a particular site, a careful choice is important. In a favourable district some types of vine will ripen the grapes as early as late August or early September, this is an open invitation to the local wasp population. The choice should therefore be restricted to types of vine that ripen consistently in early October at the earliest.

Bird damage

So much for wasps, the bird problem is a far greater threat to a vineyard. The French viticulturist does not suffer from this hazard; birds are scarce in the vine growing areas of France due perhaps to the trigger-happy and gastronomic habits of the natives. They themselves put this dearth of wild bird life down to the fact that in the vine and fruit growing areas there are no hedgerows between fields and neighbouring properties. The French cultivate every available inch of their land, thus the birds have nowhere to roost or shelter; hence their absence.

Most wild birds are protected in Britain, so if we choose to grow attractive crops such as grapes we must provide adequate protection or fail, for we cannot fall back on the shotgun.

The only 100% safe method is to net the whole vineyard. The side netting can be a permanent feature, but the top netting cannot be overwintered or even a moderate fall of snow will raze the whole affair to the ground. Therefore one must be prepared to put up the top netting, be it made of terylene, or of galvanised wire, as the grapes approach the stage in their development known as "veraison," which is when they begin to colour or become translucent and start to ripen. Avoid Ulston, as it rots in sunlight.

In the case of a small vineyard, or wall vines, protection from birds can be effected by cutting old nylon stockings into thirds, and tying them over individual bunches in the form of a bag. These make excellent preventative measures for they admit air and light, do not rot, and they drain and dry quickly after rain. Though they may be time consuming to fit they are the answer to the bird, and incidentally the wasp problem where a smaller amount of vines require adequate protection.

A further method is to purchase rolls of 2' 6" high 1" mesh wire netting, and to run this down either side of each row of vines, tying the wire together along the top above the grapes. Seat the bottom of the netting into the soil and seal the gaps at the row-ends, and thus a bird-proof netting tent is produced which is 100% effective.

One or two larger vineyards, being too extensive to net over, have introduced tame hawks to try to keep all birds away, most birds being terrified of all birds of prey. Theoretically this seems a superb idea, but we have yet to hear if this plan has proved practical.

A combination of various deterrents has been adopted with great success in a Sussex vineyard. This involved firstly leaving various tasks to accumulate in the vineyard, so that during daylight hours in the critical four to five weeks prior to harvest there would at most times be someone working there. At times when the vineyard was unattended, and according to prevailing weather conditions, either mock hawks suspended from balloons, carbide guns, or 6' yellow plastic streamers fastened to 10' canes were put to work, variation being the key to success. One could also use glitterbangs, "Flash Harry's" and fused rope bangers used for pigeons and rooks on farms.

Testing for ripeness

How can one tell when the grapes are really ripe, ripe enough to make a sound, well balanced wine? A safe rule of thumb is that they are never as ripe as they appear, and should always be left longer than one thinks!

Grapes change in appearance and character as they ripen, they lose the opaque dense powdery look, and become translucent and shiny looking as if they are about to burst apart due to being over full of juice.

Apart from appearance, tasting is an invaluable test for ripeness. Before grapes are fully ripe they are acutely bitter and solid compared with the sweet, soft, juice-laden taste of a ripe grape. Bear in mind, too, that a grape that is ripe enough for dessert purposes may still not be sufficiently ripe for wine-making; a wine grape must be possessed of a high enough sugar content to provide enough alcohol to enable the wine to store and keep well, for alcohol is the principal preservative.

Accurate tests can be made on grapes rather than leaving the judgment to one's senses, though the latter become more experienced and reliable as year follows year.

Hydrometer

A hydrometer is simply a graduated glass float which when placed in a liquid gives a reading of the density of that liquid, in this case a reading of the natural sugar content present in the grape juice. The disadvantage of using this instrument is that one has to press the juice from sufficient berries to fill the hydrometer trial glass; this is both a nuisance and often wasteful if the grapes are proved to be unready for harvesting.

In a good year the hydrometer reading may be as high as 1.085, or 85 oechsle, a natural sugar content of 2 lb. per gallon, and a potential alcohol content of 11.2 by volume. However a more average reading would be in the region of 65-75 oechsle, 1 lb. 7 oz.–1 lb. 11 oz. per gallon respectively with consequent alcohol contents of 8.4–9.7 by volume. In a poor, sunless, wet year the specific gravity reading may be as low as 40-45 oechsle; reference to the table in chapter XI will illustrate the comparative sugar and alcohol potential of such a reading. In such seasons "chaptalisation," or sugaring, will be essential to raise the total sugar content to the region of 80-90 oechsle otherwise the resultant wine will be watery, thin and sour, and will not keep.

The hydrometer is an excellent guide, but remember to deduct 2% from the reading to allow for solid matter other than sugar present in the juice.

Refractometer

An alternative method of ascertaining the exact sugar content of the grape is by using a refractometer which is an invaluable instrument much the size of a fountain pen. A drop of juice is put in this instrument; a beam of light when thrown through the thin layer of juice gives a reading of the sugar content measured within by the degree of deflection of the light caused by the sugar and solid matter. This reading is also subject to the 2% reduction due to matter other than sugar always present in the juice. Unfortunately this instrument costs around £20, but such an expense is more than justified with a vineyard where there are many such tests to be made every season.

Weather problems

The advice that one should leave the grapes on the vines until they are ripe enough is easy enough to follow in a reasonably sunny warm autumn, but unfortunately this is not always the case. Some seasons are so cold and wet that mildew and rot are apt to spread, and then all such ideals are thrown to the wind, and the crop has to be picked immediately, regardless of readiness, to avoid losing the results of a whole year's work. It is heartening to note here that surprisingly good wines can be made from terribly rotten-looking grapes providing they are treated promptly once picked, and thoroughly sterilised after pressing and prior to being yeasted.

To look on the brighter side, providing the vines have been sprayed during the growing season to prevent the formation of mildew, all is well on average in three out of four years. Choose a bright sunny day for harvesting if possible, and remember to choose the day to coincide with having sufficient time to process the grapes immediately, for if left about in baskets in damp weather they are quick to rot and spoil.

Use a sharp pruning knife or sharp efficient secateurs when harvesting the bunches to effect a clean cut; if you have a gang of helpers, have enough baskets and secateurs ready so that all can work at full capacity to save time.

Place a large receptacle, such as a large plastic dustbin at the end of each row being harvested, so that the pickers may each empty their individual baskets or buckets into this— and when full it is quickly replaced with an empty bin. This avoids wasting time and energy, and many people carrying baskets of grapes a long way, and getting under one another's feet.

Grape collection, access to and from the vineyard, transportation of the grapes to the winer, a method of tipping the fruit DOWN into the crusher to avoid lifting and carrying the heavy containers more than is essential, removal of the crushed fruit to the wine press, and lastly transferring the juice from the press to the settling tanks requires careful planning on a production-line principle beforehand. Simplicity, the shortest possible route, absence of obstructions, use of ramps instead of steps, and making sure that the equipment you buy for the winery is of sufficient size to cope with the eventual full output from the vineyard saves much trouble and anxiety later on.

CHAPTER 8

Wall vines and cloches

WHERE a south, south-east or south-west facing wall or fence can be offered, vines may be grown in an area which would otherwise be too far north or too cold for outdoor viticulture. It also allows a wider range of varieties, later ripening varieties, to be grown in recognised vinegrowing districts.

A wall offers plants grown against it shelter, radiated warmth, and a better climate than an open site, and therefore plants grown against walls in general grow better and crop more heavily than their neighbours in the open.

Support

Ample support must be provided for wall vines in the form of a framework of wires held at least 6″ from the wall by vine eyes, which are iron spikes each with a hole in one end for wire—these can be driven into the wall easily. This system is preferable by far to a trellis or cane method of support, which always rots fairly quickly, and the vine collapses, usually at a crucial time.

Planting

Preparation of the hole is even more essential for a wall vine than for the vine in the open. Plants under a wall can receive considerably more than their share of rain water, and in turn can be much drier at the roots than a vine in the open due to the protection and heat retention of a good wall.

Chapter 3 gives planting instructions. The supply of adequate drainage material is of particular importance, and if the hole or holes are considerably bigger than for other vines in the open so much the better.

Wall vines do far better if the ground surrounding the roots is cultivated, and not a path, tarmac or grassed, they can more readily avail themselves of the nourishments provided, and have no competition for the food supply.

Training the vines

Initially the treatment of the young vines is identical to that meted out to the vine in a row; at planting time cut the

Diagram 22—Training a wall vine

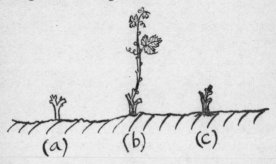

(a) A newly planted wall vine;
(b) The vine at the end of the first season;
(c) In January prune down to two buds;
(d) In second season train two shoots horizontally from the stem.

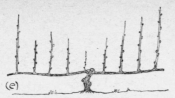

(e) In third season allow verticals to form at 12″ intervals along the two horizontals.

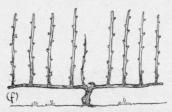

(f) In the fourth season encourage the verticals to reach full height and the vine may then crop in the fifth season.

vines down hard to leave just two or three buds on the young stub. Repeat this when the vines reach January after approximately a year in situ. This encourages active root development, and essential for strong growth in the season to come, and for good fruit production eventually.

The second season sees the beginning of the training of the vine which must be regularly attended to by tying in the growing shoots constantly as they lengthen. The accompanying diagrams will illustrate the stages in the training of wall vines better than reams of text.

Basically, if you wish to have a permanent structure, you have to decide whether you wish the arms of the grid to be horizontal or vertical to the ground. There is little to choose between the two systems, but perhaps the latter method enforces a better sap distribution when the first rush of sap runs up the vines in April. With the horizontal grid the sap is inclined to rush to the top branches and rather ignore the lower regions, resulting in little or no fruit along the lower

Diagram 23.

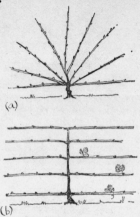

(a) A fan-trained wall vine;
(b) A horizontally trained wall vine.

horizontals. In the event of sap starvation to the lower canes with a vertically trained vine, one can always cut the vine down from the wires and lay the verticals on the ground, which centres the activity on the bent lower half of each vertical ensuring an even bud burst.

No vine should be allowed to fruit until it either reaches the third season after planting, or has reached the required size—whichever occurs first. In the spring after the vine has covered the designated area the laterals should be thinned when they have broken bud, and shown whether they are prospective bearers or not by the presence or absence of flower shoots, so that each lateral is at least one foot from another.

Secondly, do not allow more than one bunch per lateral in the first fruiting season, and if the vine is a weak specimen keep the crop very restricted untill the vine matures and thickens up.

Flowering

When the vine flowers, pinch out the growing tip four to five leaves beyond the flower shoot; this helps the flowers to set. It never comes amiss to run each flower gently through your hand to assist pollination, choosing a fine dry day.

If the weather should be wet and cold during this time, pollination is likely to be poor. A polythene cover which can be fitted over the vine will assist the setting of a good crop providing the bunches are hand pollinated since the operation would thus not be wind assisted.

Summer pruning

Keep all sub-lateral shoots pinched out as they form, to prevent the vine becoming a tangled mass of foliage and a great attraction to mildew. A spraying or powdering programme should be followed carefully, a spell of damp humid weather can so soon bring ruin. Such a task is by no means arduous; a supply of Bordeaux powder and powdered sulphur or flowers of sulphur plus a small hand puffer are all that is needed, chapter 10 deals with the suitable times to apply these preventative measures.

Spur pruning

Soon after the first crop has been gathered the first important January pruning must be tackled. Cut each lateral that has formed in the previous year, back to the main vertical or horizontal wood, leaving just two buds on the stub to provide fruiting laterals for the season to come.

This task must be repeated every January. If at any time one of the long verticals or horizontals should become unproductive, then it may be easily renewed. Encourage the shoot nearest the base or joint with the main stem to grow away well by removing any flower shoots it may throw, and by pinching off all other embryo shoots from this one long bearer. The elimination of all other growth will force all the sap and energy into this basal shoot, and it will grow away strongly.

Diagram 24.

(a)   Showing a spur before;
(b)   and after pruning leaving just *two* buds for the growth of the year to come.

The following January cut the useless old long bearer away, and tie in the new replacement cane.

Guyot, or replacement training

An alternative method of training wall vines is to adopt the Guyot system using new replacement canes each year as shown in the accompanying diagram.

This method is most suitable for the less favourable districts and colder sites, as a vine fruits more generously on annual replacements where growth is severely restricted. Obviously the vines under such conditions cannot be grown to such proportions as those which cover vast areas and are spur pruned; to counteract this one must plant more vines rather than relying on one to cover a given area in time.

Each year two replacement canes per fruiting lateral are grown, and the best is chosen each January to supplant the year-old bearer cane(s) when cut away. Remember to leave a short stub at the base of the unwanted weaker replacement cane with two or three buds to provide new canes in the year to come.

Diagram 25.

Showing how Guyot trained vines can be adapted to accommodate doors, windows, etc., note replacement canes grown to provide bearing wood for the following year.

Feeding

Wall vines benefit from generous feeding for two reasons; firstly, they have only 180° of free range in which their roots may forage for nourishment, and secondly in general they have a vary large framework to re-furbish and nourish each year compared to the highly restricted open vineyard vine. To cover such an area with grapes requires formiable energy, and the feeding provides that energy.

An autumn mulch of well rotted compost or manure is an excellent source of vigour, added to this bonemeal and hoof and horn provide long lasting benefit, wood ash in the spring is excellent, and in April and May blood from the butcher poured down a land drain let in to allow the latter access to the root system is of great value. The advice given in chapter 5 on the correction of obvious deficiencies applies here equally, a handful per spring of superphosphate and sulphate of potash will not come amiss.

Protection of fruit

When the grapes approach ripeness, it is greatly recommended that if possible the bunches be protected from the unwelcome attentions of the birds. It is a simple method to drape a net over wall grown vines, alternatively nylon stockings cut into thirds and tied in the form of small bags over each bunch are very effective, equally against the ravages of birds and wasps.

A shelter in the form of a downward sloping roof over each vine to the extent of some two foot out from the wall is most effective against hail and rain damage, and this also makes an excellent framework from which netting, or polythene to encourage ripening, may be hung.

Suggested varieties of vines for walls

Though the recommended varieties of vine are in general suitable for the designated areas, there are obvious exceptions to such advice, principally being height above sea level. Each 100 feet above sea level making the ripening of the grapes some few days later than those grown at low levels. Secondly, frost pockets can be tricky, and continuous blasting by the wind on the east coast can be disastrous.

	Wine varieties	Dessert varieties
	all varieties listed below plus ..	*all varieties listed below plus ...*
South Coast and South-west England	Pinot Meunier Pinot Noir Scheurebe	Muscat Hamburg Muscat Queen Muscat de St. Vallier White Frontignan

	Wine varieties	**Dessert varieties**
	all varieties listed below plus . . .	*all varieties listed below plus . . .*
Southern	Baco I	Brant
Counties and	Chasselas d'Or	Chasselas d'Or
West Wales	Chasselas Rose Royale	Chasselas Rose Royale
	Chasselas 1921	Chasselas 1921
	Riesling Sylvaner	Excelsior
	Seibel 13053	Oliver Irsay
	Seyve-Villard 5/276	Perle de Czaba
	Wrotham Pinot	Riesling Sylvaner
		Strawberry or
		Gros Framboisier
	all varieties listed below plus . . .	*all varieties listed below plus . . .*
Midlands and	Leon Millot	Muscat Ottonel
Wales	Marshal Joffre	Muscat de Saumur
	Noir hâtif de Marseilles	Noir hâtif de Marseilles
	Pirovano 14	Pirovano 14
	Précoce de Malingre	Précoce de Malingre
	Triomphe d'Alsace	
Favourable	Gamay hâtif des Vosges	Seigerrebe
Northerly	Madeleine Sylvaner 28/61	
sites	Madeleine Angevine 7672	
	Seigerrebe	

Cloches

Cloches are invaluable for several reasons and purposes to the vinegrower, perhaps three uses being paramount. Firstly, to the viticulturist who is already growing a particular variety or varieties in which he is particularly interested, but finds that season after season they just refuse to be cajoled into ripening their grapes; secondly, to the man who is only interested in planting the later ripening varieties of grape, or indeed in growing the better quality dessert grapes and has no glass-house for the purpose; and thirdly, and perhaps of greatest importance, to the would-be vinegrower who lives perhaps a little far north of the recognised line for viticulture, or in an unfavourable district. The ability to erect some cloches over his vines will enable him to grow them with a certainty of success, and to realise his ambition of joining the ranks of the more fortunate.

One used to be able to obtain large glass barn or tomato cloches which were excellent for the rearing and cropping of vines. Glass is naturally the best material since it allows about 90% penetration of the sun rays, and fair heat retention, whereas the horticultural Claritex or a good gauge of polythene allow correspondingly less. The latter are of course not so liable to be broken, and make excellent cloches when nailed on to a wooden framework of sufficient height to cover the Guyot bearer and the fruiting laterals properly. But before becoming brittle, Claritex has a life of two to three years when exposed to the wear and tear of continual outdoor life, and polythene a span of about nine to 12 months when it becomes somewhat translucent, very brittle and useless.

Effective cloches may be made from clear polythene sold by horticultural stores which comes in rolls of considerable length, and 6′ wide. This film, the thickest quality only, arrives bent double; one merely opens one side from the other, and rests it across the middle wire over Guyot-trained vines. The vines are now covered with a tent of clear polythene. Secure the outer bottom edges to the ground by laying boughs of wood, stones, bricks or even earth generously along the entire length. Cover the open row ends with wire or plastic netting, and you also keep the birds from the grapes. This form of cloche enables you to ripen the later varieties of grapes, perhaps particularly useful in a cold sunless summer. Not recommended for sites exposed to high wind.

Cloche training

Vines destined to be grown beneath cloches should be trained Guyot fashion, as described in chapter 3, the cloche covering the lower two wires and the bearer cane with its ensuing fruiting laterals. The replacement canes are trained in the same way as with unprotected outdoor vines, being trained through the small gap between each cloche. It is important to keep the cloches as close to one another as possible, or the object of the exercise is lost.

Diagram 26.

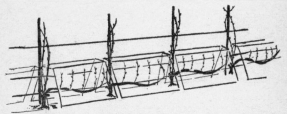

Showing how vines are accommodated beneath cloches, these vines are single Guyot trained.

The idea is to retain the heat of the sun, the grapes therefore being grown in a more favourable climate than if they were uncovered. Cloches are also a most effective bird deterrent if the ends of the rows are filled in with a sheet of glass or polythene.

The seasonal care of a cloche grown vine is exactly the same as that recommended for outdoor vines, following the Guyot method, though keeping the tips of the fruiting laterals pinched out and nipping off all sub-lateral growth is perhaps more important. Overcrowded entangled growth within the cloches can only lead to stagnant air, and such a condition is an open invitation to mildew.

Mildew prevention

Once again the advice given in a foregoing chapter on mildew and other troubles applies here, but being more susceptible than vines grown in the open vineyard where fresh air and wind in general keep trouble away, cloched vines need a strict preventative programme.

Choose a bright sunny day, when there is little wind, and, beginning at the up-wind end of each row of cloches, puff or blow powdered Bordeaux and/or powdered sulphur or flowers of sulphur between each cloche, sufficient to provide a good cover. Alternatively spray with the Zineb and soluble sulphur spray.

Cropping

A newly planted vine (or vines) does not need cloche protection until the first cropping season, generally the third year after planting. Follow chapters 3 and 4 on planting, training and pruning for these early stages.

However, after the January pruning at the beginning of the third year most young vines will be able to be cropped, and this is the time to set the cloches in place.

After the vines have cropped the cloches can be removed, cleaned and stored away until they are again required after the following January pruning session. This allows the frost and bad weather to clean and winter the vines properly, an essential to their well-being.

Weeding

Providing one keeps the interior of the cloches weedfree early in the season, in summer, particularly a dry summer, few weeds will grow due to the dry, arid condition of the soil, and the fact that few fresh weed seeds are able to contaminate the soil within. The cleaner the ground is kept, the more buoyant the air circulation, and this combined with a regular pinching out of unwanted growth does much to keep cloche-grown vines healthy and productive. Weed control can be easily effected by the use of a preparation such as GRAMMOXONE.

CHAPTER 9

Glass-house vines

HAVING a glass-house in which vines may be grown opens up wide new possibilities for the keen vinegrower. Dessert grapes of great quality may be grown easily with the protection of a cold-house, and with a little heat at the beginning and the end of the growing season, the range of dessert varieties that can be grown is tripled.

A glass-house promises the certainty of successful wine and dessert grape growing to everyone in Great Britain. So if you live in an area that is definitely impossible for outdoor vines, glass is the answer.

For an older person to whom the prospect of all the work involved with outdoor or even wall grapes is out of the question, grapes grown under glass, being concentrated in one small area, puts viticulture within their reach. When the costs involved in planting a small vineyard are compared with the erection of a glass-house, and the work required in a vineyard is compared with the time and work involved with vines under glass, for the elderly the glass-house wins hands down. The yield per vine is greater by far, and for many this is the answer.

Glass-houses

Vines will quite happily grow alongside other established plants provided they have plenty of sun and will not be shaded. Peaches, nectarines, figs and other fruits are compatible with the vine, but tomatoes, cucumbers, melons and

Diagram 27.

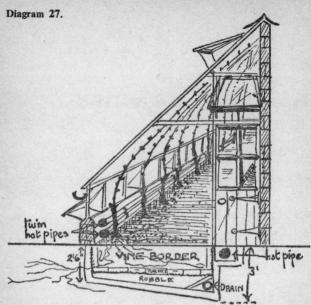

Lean-to glass vinery accommodating vines along the outer border.

Diagram 28.

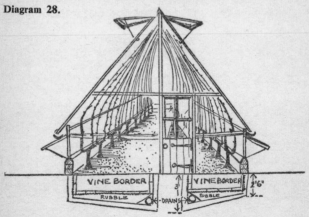

Span roofed glass vinery accommodating vines down both borders.

lettuces, requiring as they do so much humidity, should ideally not be grown in the same house; the required conditions are poles apart.

A lean-to or a span-roofed structure are both ideal for vines. With the latter, of course, twice as many vines can be accommodated, and having vents on both sides better control can be maintained over ventilation and temperature in summer. Naturally a lean-to house has better heat retention, and suffers less from heat and cold fluctuations than the more exposed span-house.

With a lean-to house a southerly or south-westerly aspect is to be preferred, and a span-roofed house ideally has its ridge running from north to south to allow longer sun penetration.

Wires

Before planting the vines it is as well to install the supporting framework of wires. These are strung vertically up the roof from the interior of the eaves to the ridge at intervals of 9″ to 12″ apart. They must not be nearer to the glass than 18″ to allow adequate room for air circulation above the vine leaves—long "vine eyes," which are specially made metal spikes with eyes in one end, will hold the wires in position.

Heating

If the aim is to grow the varieties of dessert grape that require heat at the beginning of the season, some form of heating must be installed. The cheapest to run is still probably solid fuel with a small boiler in a house at one end of the vinery, and circulating pipes laid around the house running some 2′ 6″ inside the front wall or walls and ends of the house. Electrical heating is certainly very attractive for once installed there is no work involved if you employ a thermostat to do the thinking for you, but it is certainly very expensive to run. For a small house perhaps paraffin heaters would be the answer; these can be installed with hot air pipes which would be effective. In a house of mixed vine varieties (a good plan, for one then has a supply of different types of grapes ripening over a longer period) one or two later ripening vines can be partitioned off with double polythene sheeting, with a paraffin heater to bring them on early. This eliminates wasting heat into the whole house where it is not needed.

Preparation of the border

Little success will be had from planting vines in a border that has been in existence for many years, it will probably be sour, stagnant and airless. Preparing the border properly before planting, whether in an old or new vinery, will ensure healthy vigorous vines, which for many years will crop generously, and form a vast energetic root system which helps to avoid troubles like shanking and other physiological disorders.

Drainage

Assuming that the roots are to be planted inside the house, the border should be excavated to a depth of 2′ 6″ at the back, and 3′ at the front which allows a fall for drainage purposes.

Ideally this pit should be lined throughout with bricks or breeze blocks so that complete control over the nourishment and watering of the vines can be maintained. The wider the border the better, 10 or more feet from the outside wall to the central path is excellent.

The drainage is perhaps the most important feature here, so lay a single or double row of land drains along the lowest side of the pit; these can be covered with old tiles. Extend this drain through the wall at the lower end of the house so that any excess water drains away and out of the house. A pit situated here and filled with rammed stones will act as a catch pit and prevent water laying and stagnating.

Next, level up the bottom of the pit with a drainage layer of three to four inches at the higher side to nine to ten inches at the deeper side. This should be composed of broken bricks and tiles, *old* lime and sand mortar and even clinker. Next cover this material with turves laid grass-side down before filling in with the soil.

The border soil

Though today through lack of help and facilities we have to settle for a middle of the road path rather than the ideal, and we often get away with this, the recommended plan is to stack the proposed border soil in layers with the additional fertilisers. A fibrous calcareous soil is far better than a rich loam, if however only the latter is available then coarse sand and even small clinker enable it to keep open and porous. Ideally this soil should be stacked for at least some six months prior to being used at the ratio of 10:1 to crushed old lime and sand mortar, which can be acquired when an old cottage, barn or wall is being demolished. Alternatively crushed lump chalk can be used. Added to this 10% bonfire ash, charcoal and burnt earth greatly lighten and improve the texture and porous qualities of the loam. To each ton of loam add 1 cwt. of John Innes base fertiliser and 2 cwts. of rough bonemeal. This should be turned two or three times to ensure that it is evenly mixed before use.

This is the ideal soil which will remain in good condition for many years—obviously in most cases such preparations will not be possible. In these circumstances it is advised that as much of the existing soil is removed as possible, from the border, and some good fibrous soil be filled in, with drainage material laid beneath, the latter being the most important feature of the border. Mix with this border soil as many of the recommended ingredients as possible as the soil is filled in.

To return to the new border, tread the soil lightly and evenly as it is filled in, otherwise it will sink later. The vine house is now ready for its new inhabitants, which can be planted at any time during the dormant season between October and April.

Planting

The distance apart that the vines should be planted will vary according to the type of house and whether any other plants have to be considered. If the house is span-roofed, then vines destined to carry but one rod apiece can be planted at 5' intervals. If each vine is required to take two rods then plant at 6' to 7' intervals. If you are expecting a few vines to fill a vast area and each to support many rods, divide the length of the house by the number of vines, and plant them at equal distances. In a span vinery which is to be solely devoted to vines, they can be planted along both long borders, and trained to run up the roof to meet one another at the ridge, thus filling the whole house.

Diagram 29.

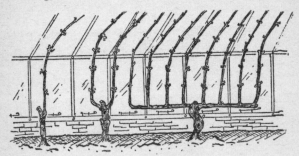

Examples of single, double and multiple canes in a span glass house.

In a lean-to house the vines can be planted along the one border nearer the glass and be trained up to the ridge. If peaches or nectarines are trained against the back wall, then the vines will have to be trained so that they do not wholly rob their companions of sun and light. In such a situation divide the house into 10' stations, and plant a vine into the border in the middle of each section. Instead of immediately training each new vine straight up the height of the house, two shoots are trained horizontally, one from each side of each vine, towards the corresponding shoots of the neighbouring vine. When this growth has been completed, vertical laterals are trained upwards, but not beyond a height that would take light and sun from the wall grown trees. Thence they are stopped, and subsequently spur pruned. Alternatively such vines could in time furnish a framework of several horizontal canes such as the first, which should not be closer together than 18".

Diagram 30.

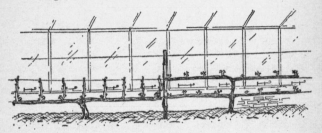

Two methods of training vines in a lean-to house where other trees such as peaches are grown against the back wall; in this way the vines are kept low to avoid shading the peaches, etc.

Remembering the needs of the wall trained plants behind, allow 18" between the top horizontal and the height limit, otherwise the wall plants will be in permanent shade in late summer when they also need all the possible sun to ripen their crop.

Training

To return to the newly planted vine or vines, which should be well watered in after planting, put a good cane in beside each vine to which it may be trained as it grows.

Given the protection and encouragement of a glass-house, the vines will grow away quickly once their roots have gained a hold, and should have reached the apex of the house by the end of the second season, if not earlier. Some varieties are very slow growers and might take three seasons, but such cases are very rare.

During this period they must be tied in at frequent intervals as they grow, first to their initial cane, and then to the roof wires, or preferably to a cane run up the height of the roof, thus providing a more substantial guide at this early stage. Soft thick silks or thick raffia are ideal for the tying in of tender young vine shoots.

All side shoots must be pinched out during this formative time for all strength and energy is required to grow the basic canes. The same rule applies to embryo flower shoots; these must be ruthlessly removed during the first two growing seasons. A vine is by no means mature enough to bear fruit whilst it is being encouraged to create permanent wood. Tendrils also must be pinched off; they can strangulate young canes very effectively, so tenaciously can they grip.

When the main cane or canes come to within 2' of the top of the roof they must be stopped, so that in years to come the ensuing growth from the top spur has enough room to develop and crop without being cramped.

Pruning

Indoor vines are pruned in mid-December when they are fully dormant. If pruned later, especially in a particularly mild winter when the sap begins to rise early, a vine can bleed very badly. Weakly, poor vines that have made little progress are treated in exactly the same manner as their outdoor counterparts; cut them down, leaving only two or three buds on the stub. These vines will catch up their more precocious companions soon enough if treated in this way; they are merely taking longer to establish a sufficient root system to support the top growth. Incidentally, if their progress is again uninspiring at the end of the second season, cut them down again, and the third season will surely see them catch up their neighbours.

Vines that have grown away strongly during the first season are, however, allowed to keep two thirds of their single or twin canes if this amount be well ripened, nut brown in colour and pencil thick. If less than two-thirds answers this description, then cut back to mature cane. Unripe cane is denoted by its greeny, yellow colour and thin appearance.

During the dormant season open all windows and ventilators to allow the vines to winter properly—a few frosts do untold good in that they destroy certain pests and mildew spores. This applies every winter—the vines should be exposed to the cold until bud burst is imminent. When this occurs they must be protected from the cold and frost, so close the windows and ventilators on cold days and every night, but on fine days allow as much air circulation as possible.

Summer pruning in second season

The vines will break bud and grow away in the late spring of the second season when water can be given as and when conditions are suitable—during dry buoyant conditions, but not during muggy, wet, foggy or humid weather.

Laterals are now allowed to form at 1' intervals, all those in between being pinched out. The remaining laterals are pinched out after two to three leaves; these are to form the spurs from which the fruit of the third season is produced. Keep all sub-laterals, tendrils and embryo flower shoots pinched out, and by the end of the second season the majority of the vines should have produced ripe cane to 3' from the roof apex—and will be able to carry a drop the following season. Keep the vines well aired during the first and second season, not having to ripen grapes at this stage, plenty of fresh air keeps the vines free from disease.

Winter pruning and care

In mid-December the lateral stubs are cut back to leave just two buds on each to provide fruiting shoots for the year to come, spray the vines with a 5% tar oil solution, thoroughly wetting the vines, walls and glass to eliminate vine pests and disease spores. Next fork and gently brush some soil from the roots of the vines, and apply some well rotted manure, bonemeal, wood ashes and some vine fertiliser to the soil at this lower level, and replace the top soil, treading it firmly back into place. At this stage an earthenware land drain can be inserted beside each vine, through which the vine can be supplied with water and liquid fertiliser when necessary during the year, and with liquid blood from the butcher each

111

spring which stimulates growth and a good healthy leaf structure.

Pre-bud burst

In March or April there comes a time when the vine buds quite suddenly swell and begin to burst, when this threatens, all windows are shut and the vines should be sprayed with water daily, also the border and path, to increase the humidity and encourage an even bud break.

Certain varieties of vine are more apt to shoot and crop well only on the spurs furthest from the ground at the expense of the spurs nearer the main stem. To allow this to occur without preventative measures would mean that the vine would only be cropping at half its capacity, which is a waste of time and space.

To ensure that bud break occurs evenly up the entire length of the bearer cane, cut all the ties holding the vine to the wall and roof wires, and lay the vine on the house border. This creates an exaggerated arch between the ground stem and the further extremity, and the buds situated on the arch will break away first. The vine can now be tied up into place once more.

When the shoots are between 1″ and 2″ in length it can be ascertained which are the better prospective fruit bearers; some will be barren, others may have just one miserable embryo flowet shoot, whereas others will be well endowed. Keep the two best shoots, rubbing all others off at their hilt. As the two remaining shoots develop, one will show more promise than the other; the poorer must be pinched off, leaving one shoot per spur. Not more than one bunch of grapes must be allowed from each spur in this, the first fruiting season, but one may allow progressively more bunches as the vine grows older.

Flowering

In due course the minute bunches-to-be will come into flower, heralded by the most fragrant, delicate scent. Spraying of the vines with water must cease immediately, but it is necessary for there to be a humid atmosphere in the house at this vital stage so the border and path should be kept damp but not wet. On fine days open the door and ventilators until noon so that airy, bright conditions prevail, and a breeze blowing through the house helps pollination. As near noon as possible close the door and nearly shut the ventilators, and lightly spray the floor and border to raise the humidity—to follow this advice does much to help this delicate operation to be successful. The flowers are not, however, ready for pollination immediately they open, not until the stigma is in the right condition to receive the pollen from the anthers.

To assist pollination further one can gently run the flower racemes through the hand, spreading pollen from one variety to another. This greatly assists those vines that are shy setters, particularly with their own pollen, because a good set is only obtained when pollen from other varieties is used— hence the need for more than one type of vine in a vinery. To illustrate this point Muscat of Alexandria sets well with the pollen from Black Hamburg, whereas Chasselas Rose, a very free setter, will set adequately with the pollen it produces itself.

After pollination, the house may be well aired every day from the early morning, particularly during fine hot weather, and closed just before sundown each day if possible to keep the warmth trapped inside for the night. Water when necessary, not during the heat of the day but in the early morning on fine days.

Thinning

A pair of long nosed grape thinning scissors are vital for this task, which should be tackled soon after the grapes have set. Try to visualise the bunch as it will be, leave plenty of grapes at the shoulders and enough to keep the shape of the bunch, but remove most of the interior berries, and leave each berry that is to remain a pencil width from its neighbour. This may sound very drastic, but when the bunch is nearly ripe you will probably have to thin yet again; so fast do the berries swell, and so overcrowded do they become that one finds that sometimes three thinnings are not enough! Never

Diagram 31.

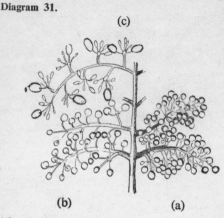

A bunch of grapes (a) before thinning; (b) after thinning; and (c) a branchlet of MUSCAT OF ALEXANDRIA that has set poorly, only a few berries having been pollinated.

touch the berries or the bloom will be spoilt; hold the bunches during thinning with a "Y" shaped twig.

Mildew prevention

Being indoors where air circulation is comparatively hampered, vines are more prone to mildew especially during damp, muggy weather, therefore a more rigorous preventative programme must be employed than suggested for outdoor vines. Always have a supply of Bordeaux powder and powdered sulphur or flowers of sulphur ready to hand and puff the combined powders in a puffer or blower at a ratio of two of Bordeaux to one of sulphur at fortnightly intervals. If the weather is humid this can be more frequent.

Immediately after the flowers have set and the berries begin to form, puff sulphur into every bunch to prevent these from becoming affected. The protection given by this action will penetrate into the centre of every bunch, which is impossible to accomplish at a later stage when the berries have developed, and will last until the grapes are harvested.

Cropping

Some two or three months after pollination the earlier varieties of grapes will be ripening; again an illustration of the advantage of having several varieties of grape is the prolonged harvesting season which can last from August to November quite easily. During this formative period the vines can be fed with liquid manures and even blood, for the vine is ever hungry and much appreciates generous nourishment. Once the berries near ripening and become either translucent if they are white grapes, or begin to show signs of colour if they are black, all feeding should cease, and watering should soon follow suit. To water profusely at this point results in burst grape skins, which is a tragic waste of a whole season's love and care. If the roots of the vine are outside the house, steps should be taken to cover the root area with polythene sheeting or corrugated iron to shoot the water off.

Keep the vinery very well aired during this time in the day, and if the season has been poor, and the later varieties refuse to ripen, heat may be provided with a screen to concentrate heat on the particular vine to bring them on—this is particularly beneficial at night when the temperatures drop low in the autumnal months.

Harvesting

Taste will tell whether the grapes are ripe or not, they are never as ripe as they look and benefit much from being left on the vine as long as possible during which time a gradual mellowing is taking place.

Protect the crop against wasps and birds as recommended in chapter 6; sometimes these marauders can threaten the crop seriously. When the ventilators should be open daily and birds start to attack, wire netting can be tacked across the apertures so that ventilation is not impaired. Failing this, netting will have to be employed, or nylon stocking bags can be tied over each bunch, a tedious but rewarding task.

Renovating an old vine

Should a vine become too old to be productive, the best plan is usually to dig it out, renew the border soil and replant. Should this prove impracticable, old vines can quite easily be completely renovated and regain some of their former productivity.

Whether the vine in question be trained vertically, or horizontally with many verticals, the principles of renewing are the same.

At the beginning of the season allow one or two shoots from as near the bottom of the vine as possible to grow on unchecked, remove all fruit, tendrils and lateral growth from these leaders, so that all energy is devoted to their extension. Meanwhile, it is advisable, though not vital, to restrict the cropping and other growth of the vine during this season to channel all resources into the renewal programme. In the ensuing December all the old woody part of the vine can be sawn off a few inches above the new replacement canes, and the wound painted with lead paint or neat tar oil. Thus in one, or perhaps two, seasons if the renewal growth rate is slow, a new vine has been created from the old. Close attention to the border will further improve the outlook and prospects of the vine.

To conclude

Before listing varieties of vine that can be planted under glass, there are one or two points that should be stressed.

Good border conditions are vital for the continuing success of the venture, and attention to pruning, thinning of the shoots, pollinating and the all important supply of fresh air, feeding and watering just make the difference between success and failure.

The foregoing advice on the year's work in an indoor vinery is repeated annually. To grow grapes properly and to their best advantage is undoubtedly a task that demands daily attention during most of the growing season. The house has to be opened in the morning, the path and border sprayed with the hose to keep up the humidity, and the house has to be closed at night except during hot weather in July and August. There are obviously times in the year when several hours a day are required, particularly during pruning, winter spraying, fumigating against mildew, and manuring and dressing the border, all December jobs that are oddly enough enjoyable. It is the close season for all outdoor tasks, and to have plenty to do under the cover of the glass-house keeps the close-knit continuity of the stages in the care of the vine very alive in one's mind. If these tasks are well and efficiently carried out, the year to come should be a successful and healthy season for the vinery; December and January certainly being the vital axis around which the success of the remainder of the year revolves.

Other busy periods in the vinery year are during disbudding, pollination, tying in the tender young shoots and in due course stopping them, and, most tedious of all, the grape thinning, unfortunately a necessary evil.

Indoor grape production is a dedication, but there are few more rewarding ways of spending time, particularly when one reflects that for up to three months of the year one can have a fresh bunch of home-grown grapes on the table every day; surely this is the height of luxury!

Varieties of vine recommended for the cold-house

Black Hamburg

The most commonly grown black dessert grape in this country, bunches are large, and round or conical in shape, berries large, juicy, firm and sweet; easy to grow and an early ripener. Good setter and very well recommended.

Buckland Sweetwater

A white grape, ripening to green/gold; of excellent sweet juicy flavour; berries large and round or oval, and the bunches are well shouldered, large and cone shaped. A vine with long,

117

long associations in this country. A good setter, again well recommended, and early ripening.

Foster's Seedling

A green/gold grape, of juicy sweet melting flavour, again a good setter, berries large and round or oval, bunches are of good shape and large in size. Well recommended, and early ripening.

Chasselas d'Or (Royal Muscadine, Fendant, Chasselas de Fontainebleau)

This is a truly excellent cold-house variety, berries greeny/gold and round, bunches are long and can become very large, and when allowed to ripen really well the flavour is delicious. Recommended, and very early ripening. CHASSELAS 1921 is slightly earlier.

Chasselas Rose Royale

Similar in every way to its close relation above, but the grapes ripen to a deep pinky/red if allowed access to the rays of the sun while ripening. Early ripening and well recommended.

Mrs. Pince

A black grape, berries are oval and large, flavour sweet, rich and muscat flavoured. Bunches are cylindrical, long and large, the grapes are good free setters, and this is a well recommended variety that ripens early in the south.

Muscat Hamburg

A black grape, of excellent rich, melting juicy flavour, said by many to supersede Black Hamburg in every way; but being liable to shanking and producing many seedless grapes it does need care; hand cross pollination preferably with MADRESFIELD COURT: grows well if in-arched on to and grown on BLACK HAMBURG stock. Berries of medium size and oval bunches medium sized and conical. Fairly late ripener in cold-house, but suitable southern counties.

Varieties of vine recommended for house heated in spring and autumn

Alicante (Meredith's Alicante)

A black grape, with large oval berries of good flavour; bunches are thick shouldered, attractive but have a short shank with results in the berries appearing to cluster around the cane, therefore early thinning is essential. Good setter, and will ripen without heat in southern counties, but best flavour is obtained when heat is used to ripen the grapes.

Appleby Towers

A black grape, of rich juicy flavour; berries are large, oval and leathery, the bunches being of medium size and conical. A good setter, needs heat to begin and finish, of excellent quality.

Canon Hall Muscat

A white grape, of juicy, tender, melting muscat flavour, berries round and of good size, with long conical bunches. A very poor setter, hand pollinate with MADRESFIELD COURT. Needs experienced care to bring out the best with this variety which being thinner skinned than its parent MUSCAT OF ALEXANDRIA is truly delicious when well grown. Needs heat early and late.

Madresfield Court

A blue/green grape of rich, juicy tender muscat flavour, berries are oval and large, bunches are very large and taper well. This grape sets well, and appreciates heat to finish. Delicate grower compared to more robust varieties, but ripens crop and wood well.

Mrs. Pearson

A white/gold grape, firm, with rich juicy muscat flavour; berries round and large, bunches well shouldered and conical. Being a late ripener this grape requires heat at beginning and end of season. Vine grows well and is of tough appearance.

Muscat of Alexandria

A white/gold grape of sweet semi-juicy firm muscat quality; berries oval and large, bunches loose and long. A poor setter, hand pollinate with BLACK HAMBURG or FOSTER'S SEEDLING; will ripen without heat in southern counties, but to bring out the best heat is needed. A grape of great quality and flavour.

Muscat Hamburg

As described in cold-house section. This grape will grow without heat, but perhaps does better with early and late heat. Superb quality and first class flavour.

Prince of Wales

A black grape, of juicy tender muscat flavour, berries oval and of medium size, bunches low shouldered and long. This grape prospers if grown on young wood rather than on age-old spurs, it is a fairly good grape but is likely to be mildew prone.

Rain deflection from wall and glasshouse vines

Where vines are grown against walls, particularly building walls, and also when glasshouse vines have their roots planted outside, it is important that during the vital final few weeks of ripening, between the period when the grapes begin to colour or become translucent and the harvest date, that no rainwater gains access to the roots. Should this occur, the grapes will split with the sudden on-rush of fresh sap, this being an open invitation to mildew and other ills.

To prevent this disaster, simply lay a sheet or two of corrugated iron against the wall at an angle of 45° over the area of ground occupied by the roots. This will shoot all rainwater beyond the root territory, thus the crop will be saved in a wet autumn.

CHAPTER 10

Vine propagation and grafting

VINES can be quickly and easily multiplied by striking cuttings obtained from ripe nut-brown wood from the January pruning operations. Vines can be propagated in a variety of ways, the choice of method depending firstly on the amount of suitable wood available, secondly, on the amount of vines required, and thirdly, the conditions for striking that one is able to offer the cuttings.

If you have plenty of prospective cuttings available, and have the empty ground in which to strike and grow on outdoor long cuttings, this is by far the easiest and most troublefree method. If on the other hand you have a very special vine or two, and wish to make as many new vines from this as quickly as possible, then short cuttings struck and grown on in a pot, or individual eyes rooted in pots or in upturned turves are the answer. By these two methods more vines are obtained from a small amount of wood, and can be grown in a controlled atmosphere away from the vagaries of the elements— preferably in a propagating frame. By so doing one can enjoy 100% success.

Vine cuttings can strike as readily as blackcurrant slips, and when the weather is kind 100% success can be obtained with some varieties. Needless to say when the weather decides to do its worst, some assistance is required to protect these cuttings from an untimely end.

Long cuttings

A vine produces suitable wood for propagation purposes from the third and ensuing year's growth, earlier prunings are nearly always too thin and poor and thus are more than likely to rot in the ground. After having pruned away the unwanted old bearer canes and the lesser replacement canes as suggested in chapter 4, you are now provided with material from which cuttings can be made. Tear all the fruiting laterals off the long bearer, each with a heel, then cut the rough edges off the heel to discourage rotting, and either trim the unripe top portion off if the lateral is no more than 1' in length, or if the later is nearly 18" long it may be cut into two cuttings, after having removed the unwanted tip. The long bearer may now be cut into 9–12" lengths—though not so productive as the one year wood, this two year wood may well root at a rate of 50% or thereabouts. Lastly, cut up the year old lesser replacement cane. From this it will be realised that quite a few such cuttings can be produced from just one vine.

Diagram 32.

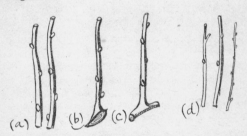

Three suitable types of long cuttings:

(a) A cutting from an ordinary cane
(b) A cutting with a heel or foot
(c) A shoot cutting
(d) Unsuitable cuttings

Before progressing further, note the types of wood that make successful cuttings, and the wood that should be avoided. Only attempt to strike sound pencil thick nut-brown coloured material, it is a waste of time trying to strike lesser wood out of doors; it just rots away in the ground.

If the weather in January, immediately following the pruning operations, is mild and open, then these long cuttings may be planted at once. In the colder, more exposed areas of Great Britain however, it is advisable to tie these cuttings into bundles of 25 to 30, label them with an indelible pencil or pen, and bury them in boxes of damp sand in the potting shed or under the glass-house staging until March when climatic conditions become more tractable.

Diagram 33.

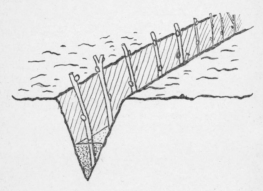

Long cuttings laid in an outdoor trench; note sand in base of trench to assist quick rooting.

To plant cuttings take out a long V-shaped trench with a spade, of sufficient depth to take the cuttings, fill the bottom 3″ of the trench with sharp potting sand, and proceed to lay the cuttings along one side of the trench. If you wish to take extra care, the bottom end of each cutting can be dipped first in water, then in to hormone rooting powder prior to planting.

Next fill in the trench, and tread firmly along on either side of the row of cuttings. No more than an inch or so of each cutting should be showing above the ground. Lastly, put a label to each row showing the variety therein.

Whether the long cuttings are January or March planted, the former preferably, careful watch must be kept for drought conditions once growth begins and the top buds swell and shoot.

The cutting is at its most vulnerable with top growth making progress as it always does before any root system has formed. A period of drought in spring, with its attendant winds and hot sunshine, can quickly scorch and dry the life out of a rootless cutting; therefore during such conditions one should aim to give the vine rows a spray with the hose *before* the sun gains any heat in the morning. Applied later in the day, combined with the sun rays, scorching will be increased, while evening spraying encourages damp conditions to linger overnight which could be an open invitation to mildew attack.

Early morning spraying combined with frequent hoeing to keep the soil open, aerated and weedfree will see the vines safely through this hazardous period. Cuttings do require sun, but they also need a certain amount of humidity in the soil to encourage rooting. The sand at the foot of the trench eliminates foot rot, assists drainage and provides an excellent medium for the young roots to gain a hold on life.

Once these vines start to grow away strongly this can be taken as a sign that some functioning roots have formed, and all worries are over, for the vine will never now look back. This stage will occur from late June to late July, and cuttings that have no outwatds sign of life by late August are certain non-starters and can be pulled up.

Pot cuttings

Vine cuttings can easily be rooted in pots either with or without bottom heat, using size six or seven pots, several cuttings can be rooted in one pot which saves space.

After scrubbing the pots well, put a drainage layer of crocks in the bottom, and then mix up a compost of two parts soil, one part peat and one part coarse sand. Half fill the pots, then dip each cutting in water followed by a dip in hardwood hormone rooting powder. Insert five or six cuttings of 6–7″

in length around the edge of each pot, making sure that each has the required three eyes. Fill up the remainder of the pot with the soil, firming well all the time, and lastly give each pot a thorough watering, and insert the appropriate label. With bottom heat, these cuttings will begin to shoot almost immediately, and correspondingly quickly will establish a good root system. The advantages here are that one is able to control the growing medium and conditions entirely, and the success rate is usually excellent. The vines root more quickly than their outdoor counterparts. Obviously where vast numbers of cuttings are required this method would not be practicable, but for a few cuttings, perhaps of the more special and unusual varieties, it is both an interesting and rewarding pastime.

Diagram 34.

Rooting cuttings in a pot.

Keep the soil damp, but not wet, and if the pots are in a propagating frame some brown paper shading can be laid over the cuttings until the buds have burst. Without heat, to insert the entire pot into an upside down polythene bag creates the conditions of a miniature glass-house thus encouraging growth. This also prevents transpiration to a great extent and lessens the necessity of watering.

Vine eyes

Where there is a very small amount of vine wood available for propagation, individual eyes or buds may be used.

They can be rooted either in pots or on upturned turves, the

Diagram 35.

Rooting vine eyes in pots and on inverted turves, and pegged down with hairpins.

latter being planted out without disturbing the vine once the roots are established within.

Use only ripe nut-brown coloured pencil thick cane, and cut away all wood between the buds leaving each with an inch of wood on either side of the eye. Scrape away a sliver of cane from the underside to assist rooting.

Diagram 36.

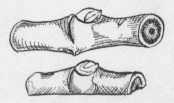

A vine eye before and after preparation for rooting.

Fill some pots with a mixture of soil at a ratio of 50% to peat at 25% and coarse sand at 25%, putting some crocks in the bottom of the pots to assist drainage. Peg one or more eyes into the soil with hair pins or crossed sticks, sinking them into the soil well and leaving just the top third of the cane clear of the soil together with the vine eye. Give bottom heat, the roots will quickly issue from the underside of the cane soon after the top growth has emerged from the bud.

To use turves, cut the turf into 6″ squares some 3″ deep, the soil of which should ideally be of a light, sandy nature which encourages quick rooting. Scoring a groove into the underside soil, the eyes may be laid into this furrow, one to each turf, and pegged down with hair pins or crossed slips of stick. Vine eyes can be dipped into water followed by dipping the scored underside of the eye into hardwood hormone rooting powder to assist and encourage quick rooting.

There are certain advantages to be gained by rooting vines by either of the aforementioned methods. Firstly, when they are due to be planted out into their permanent homes, little or no disturbance of the root system occurs resulting in a quicker take and unhalted progress when compared with the efforts of a transplanted vine rooted and grown in the open-air nursery bed. This is perhaps more important with indoor vines where headway is required as quickly as possible.

Secondly, the environment and climate wherein pot and turf cuttings are grown can be wholly controlled as opposed to the hazardous and unpredictable conditions that can beset the outdoor cutting. Thirdly, bottom heat can be provided to vines raised in pots and turves, which greatly speeds up the precarious period when top growth is forming before there is a root system to support the precocity of the shoot and leaf formation.

Layering

Yet another way to increase numbers of vines is by layering. Layering is a method of propagation by way of using material that is attached to the parent plant so that during the rooting period the cane is still receiving sustenance from its host.

Diagram 37.

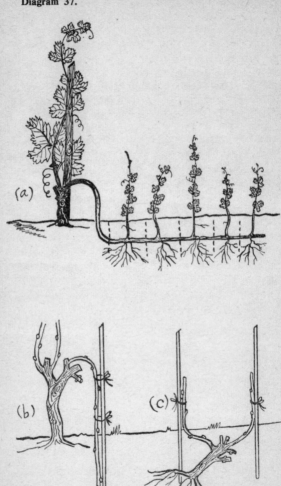

(a, b & c) Three methods of layering vines.

Simply lay an entire young cane just beneath soil level as shown in the diagram, and from most of the buds or eyes on the upper side will issue forth young vine growth. Meanwhile on the underside roots will be busily forming, encouraged by the unceasing food supply from the parent plant. Such a method is quick and most effective. To hold the cane beneath the ground, either pegs or heavy stones should be used to keep the cane firmly in place or it will spring back into an upright position.

When the top growth reaches a height of a foot or so, it may be assumed that the roots are functioning, a brief examination will verify this one way or the other. The layer may now be severed from the parent, and can itself be cut into sections each possessed of an aerial shoot and a root system thus providing several plants per layer.

After care of young vines

Once young vines have rooted and begun to grow away well it is as well to keep the beds weeded and hoed to reduce the competition for the soil nutrients and sun. Some vines will make quite considerable growth and should have a cane inserted beside them and be tied in as they grow. Liquid manure watered in at this stage but no later than late August is most beneficial and encouraging.

Grafting

Why graft a vine when it can perfectly well form roots of its own? It must be agreed that this is so, but there are a few cases where a vine grows and fruits better on roots of a variety other than its own.

Firstly, one finds that certain indoor dessert vines grow and crop notoriously badly on their own roots, and in such cases if one wishes to grow these particular vines to the best of their ability, grafting them on to the recommended rootstock is the answer.

Secondly, a vine, though outwardly robust and vigorous, is a being of delicate balance. There are a great number of varieties of vine grown all over this globe, and there are a combination of factors, namely soil, climate and geographical location which either suit or do not suit each variety. A particular vine grown in one particular area will produce an exquisite wine, whereas the same vine sited in another area can never produce other than the plainest vin ordinaire. This problem can sometimes be solved by grafting the vine grown in the latter area producing the poor wine on to a rootstock known to thrive in the soil of the district. There are a variety of rootstocks, all suiting different soils, and where someone's livelihood depends on the production of a good wine one may be sure that the rootstock best suited to the vine and the soil will be chosen.

Thirdly, following the ravages of phylloxera in Europe in the 1860s when the vineyards of Europe and further afield were completely laid waste by this horrific beetle, the only answer lay in grafting every vine on to American phylloxera-resistant rootstocks. Therefore to the Europeans this became a reluctant necessity if there were to be any future for wine growing.

So far, apart from two known outbreaks in recent years, we are apparently free of Phylloxera in England, and outwardly there is no obvious specific need to plant grafted vines. However, before deciding one way or the other, there are certain points worthy of serious consideration.

Firstly, the argument may be raised that the risk of Phylloxera spreading is virtually negligible since English vineyards are few and far between. But surely the risk lays in this very scarcity factor; growers will happily travel hundreds of miles annually to visit other vinegrowers and their vineyards. Also, it is not generally realised that during its winged stage, the Phylloxera can fly many hundreds of miles.

Secondly, the older and purist generations of vinegrower, and indeed wine drinker, maintain that the yield from the ungrafted vine was far heavier, and that pre-grafted wine was infinitely superior. To further support this claim, we hear that in Phylloxera-free areas of France, vines are once again being planted on their own roots. These claims are hotly refuted by others; there is obviously scope here for unbiased research!

For the commercial vineyard, is it worth while risking considerable initial and annual capital expenditure in the trusting hope that Phylloxera will not at some time become endemic in England? An added advantage is that there is a wide choice of rootstocks available to suit any soil type, including up to 60% rank chalk.

To conclude, it would appear that for the commercial vineyard, grafted vines are the answer; but if one is growing vines for amateur use, the choice is wide open, and the purist can enjoy his full and free rein.

Principles of grafting

There are many methods of grafting, the ways and means by which the rootstock may be joined to the scion are legion and are best explained by way of diagrams.

The principles vital for success in this most intricate and delicate task are similar in all cases.

The stock or rootstock is the variety of vine chosen due to its suitability to the soil of the locality—the scion being the variety of vine you wish to propagate. The resulting vine will grow the same variety of grapes as those of the scion, but will follow the growth behaviour pattern of the rootstock. A rootstock is chosen for its suitability to the soil, and it can also be chosen to impart more vigorous characteristics into a weak growing vine that produces worthwhile grapes, or conversely, to dwarf or lessen the vigour of an over-vigorous variety that also produces worthwhile grapes. The permutations are endless, and very interesting, making this a most absorbing study.

Grafting is an art; You are either able to graft or you are not; it emanates from an affinity with the plant, with its needs and requirements at this, the most difficult of all tasks. Success may or may not come after many failures, and it is by trial and error that one learns.

To begin with, one should work with straight wood of the same thickness if possible, and always sound ripe wood $\frac{1}{3}''-\frac{1}{2}''$ in diameter. An exact, correct fit at the union or joint is imperative. Once the two are cut accurately and fitted together so that the layer wherein the sap rises, the cambium layer, of both scion and stock fit together exactly, the union

131

can be bound with stout raffia and then covered with grafting wax to prevent the joint from drying out.

Bench grafting

Bench grafting is to join two pieces of cane together, the stock being unrooted. As soon after pruning as possible, gather together the canes from the vines you wish to graft together. Cut the stocks into normal cutting lengths of three or four buds each, and the scions to 2″ long, each with a single bud. There are various ways of making the joints between the two as shown in the accompanying diagrams, the important factor being that the cut curfaces must be absolutely

Diagram 38—Grafting

(a) Whip and tongue, or "English" grafting

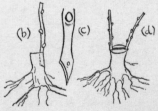

(b) Simple crown graft

(c) A scion prepared for plain cleft grafting

(d) Plain cleft graft using two scions

132

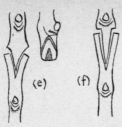

(e) A plain cleft graft

(f) A cleft graft with
     shoulders

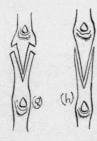

(g) Cleft graft with
     angled shoulders

(h) Hollow cleft graft

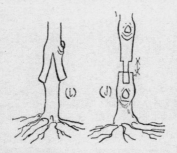

(i) Saddle grafting

(j) Mortice grafting

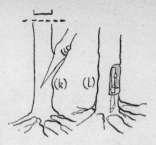

(k) Oblique grafting   (l) Side graft

(m) Bud grafting   (n) holding a bud graft in
                                    place on the stock

(o) Majorca bud grafting

true to one another. If at any point there is a gap between
them then the graft simply will not take. It is of no use to
just cut the two roughly with a penknife, or a concave cut
will be made on each which will never join because there will
be a gap.

Once the two are joined, bind them with raffia and wipe
them over with grafting wax or melted paraffin wax, and then
lay them between 3″ layers of clean, damp but not wet, sand
in a box in a warm room. The temperature should ideally be
about 70°F, and the humidity should be kept high. Keep the
sand damp, but not wet, and in about a month a weak union
will have formed; this process is called stratification.

When the weather warms, these grafted cuttings can be
lifted, and planted with great care out into sand bottomed
V trenches to root. Lay them into the trench at 45°, and fill

in the trench covering the graft well with soil, treating them as tenderly as you possibly can at this stage.

Grow them on for two years in the cutting bed, remembering to scrape the soil from the graft each July and cut away all the roots emanating from the scion and re-cover the graft. When they are planted out into the vineyard, keep the graft *above* soil level, but pull loose soil up around the graft *after* cropping and pull it away when growth begins in the spring.

Cleft grafting

Here the stocks are already established rooted plants of possibly a few years old, either grown for the purpose, or perhaps of some variety of unsuitable or uncertain cropping habit on to which a more suitable variety may be joined.

In early March cut the stock off level with the ground, or as near to the ground as possible according to the type of graft being used, and prepare the stock accordingly. The most common method practised is to hold a knife across the cut surface, and force or knock it down some 2″. Into this split, the true sided cut surface of a 3″ scion is slipped, making sure that the cambium layers are in contact at least on one side. Bind the graft firmly with raffia, and then cover the whole with topsoil the top of the scion being just below the surface. Treat henceforth as suggested before, remembering to gently remove the soil in July or August, and cut off the scion roots before pulling the soil up again.

Inarching or approach grafting

This method of grafting is particularly useful in a vinery where it may be used to serve a variety of purposes. If an indoor dessert variety proves to be a particularly poor grower, or alternatively, a variety grows too vigorously to be contained within the house and crops poorly, or thirdly, perhaps you have an interesting new vine you wish to crop as soon as possible, then this method is invaluable. The prospect of having one or two rootstocks in a vinery with several varieties grafted on to each is an interesting thought.

135

Here both varieties of vine are growing rooted specimens, though the prospective stock may be a stout well established vine, and the scion-to-be a young one or two year old pot grown vine which has been cut back hard in the previous year to produce a tough young rod. At the same time a strong young cane is encouraged at the right level on the stock vine. The most successful way of consummating the union between the two canes is the whip and tongue method. In this the bark of the two canes is sliced so that two ovals of some 2″ in length are presented to one another. Secondly, an upward cut is made into the scion opposite a downward tongue on the stock. The two are fitted into one another, thus pulling

Diagram 39.

Inarching one vine to another.

the two flat oval surfaces together, the whole is bound with broad raffia and covered with grafting wax.

This graft will take from two to three months to become firm, and during this period the binding must be under constant surveillance so that it does not become too tight as the rods quickly swell. Do not rashly cut the lower half of the scion and the upper stock away immediately the suggested time is up, but gradually remove the laterals above the graft on the stock vine to encourage the sap and energy to be drawn into the scion. Also cut a notch into the scion below the point of graft, and gradually increase this cut weekly until it is completely through at about the twelfth week.

When you are sure that the graft is firm and well knit, the stock vine can be severed above the graft, and the graft is complete.

To conclude here, Black Hamburg makes an excellent stock vine and imparts a vigorous habit to the growth rate of the grafted vine. The stock does not inflict any flavour, quality, earliness or lateness into the resulting grapes, merely affecting the vigour or growth rate of the vine to which it is supplying lifeblood.

Growing a vine in a pot

Apart from the fact that it is very interesting to grow several varieties of vines in pots, thus enabling one to have a few types of grapes available for eating with little effort, such a method is ideal for the smaller greenhouse where the whole or part of the inner area cannot be spared for overall vine culture.

Once the vine or vines have reached their second season, transfer them to larger pots into which a good layer of crocks has been placed, and plant them in a compost consisting of plenty of peat, sharp sand, wood ash, bone meal and if possible a proportion of crumbled well rotted manure or compost. During this second season encourage one good cane upwards and stop it at about 6' tying it in to a cane as it grows.

In December prune the unripe end off this cane, for unripe wood merely encourages mildews. Make, or have made, a metal or wooden pot vine-frame as shown in the accompanying diagram, and put this in place in the pot. Tie the upper end of the cane around the top of the frame, and when growth starts in the spring, complete the circle of the frame as the cane grows pinching out the end of this cane when the whole has been circumscribed. Fruit can be allowed during this season due to the restricted nature of this method, but allow a token crop only if the vine is to have a future; larger crops can be allowed each year.

Stop the laterals two leaves beyond each fruit cluster, and keep sub-laterals strictly pinched out in order to concentrate energy where it is most needed.

Prune such vines in December, spur pruning is the best method here, remembering to leave two buds on the base of each spur to provide for the following year. Pot grown vines need re-potting each December, for in one year the roots will have extracted all the food matter from the soil; knock the

Diagram 40.

A pot grown vine, ideal for the smaller glass-house.

pot gently all round, and gently extract the root mass as a whole. Knock the soil from the roots, and in most cases provide a larger pot each year, put in plenty of broken crocks, and press fresh soil and the aforementioned additives firmly around the roots with a thick stick, shaking the vine gently to ensure that there are no air gaps which attract rot.

Follow this pattern year after year until the vine becomes too old and unwieldy, when either a fresh cane is encouraged up from the cep or stem of the vine, or a complete replacement is advised if the yield has started to drop.

CHAPTER 11

Making wine from grapes

WINE is simply fresh grape juice, fermented by yeast, which feeds on the sugars it contains, turning them into alcohol and carbon dioxide.

The process involved in the making of a white wine as opposed to a red wine is initially different. To make white wine the juice is pressed out and fermented, whereas for red wine the whole "pulp," including the stems is fermented for a period, to extract the necessary colour from them.

Due to Britain's geographical position and climate it is fair to say that in general it is not possible to grow the varieties of black grape in the open to enable us to create really full bodied red wines of character; the limited varieties of black grapes we manage to encourage to ripen sufficiently to make into wine make a thin, acid, red wine. Even if matured for a few years in wood to mellow and mature they will never improve sufficiently to become more than a rather thin, poor wine. In a good year a very fair wine may be made, but one's energies are far better spent making white wines which can be very good indeed if well made. Some may dissent, but one has to admit that English grown black grapes somehow do not possess that essential body which is so necessary a part of a red wine. To confirm this, consider the Continent: all the wine made in the northern half of this land mass is white; the wines of the Rhine, Moselle, Alsace, Champagne, Chablis, Pouilly Fumé, and areas along the

139

north bank of the river Loire, with the exception of the Anjou Rosé, are all white; red wines are only grown successfully in the more southern sunnier, and hotter areas. Surely we must pay some attention to the hundreds of years experience of the French and German vinegrowers.

One would hesitate before advising anyone to plant black grape vines en masse, for in nine years out of 10 the resultant wine would be very disappointing.

There are many varieties of white grape available these days to suit most areas of the country, easy to grow, very early ripening, and regular croppers even in poor years. Wines of good quality can be made providing scrupulous attention is paid to cleanliness of the equipment throughout the fermentation and storage period. White wines may also be made from black grapes for the juice of a black grape is usually white, the colour being contained in the skins. Champagne is made in part from the Pinot Noir which is a black grape, a variety also used in Burgundy for making red wine.

If black grapes are to be used to make white wine, they must be processed and pressed after being crushed very quickly or the juice will be coloured slightly, and will then have to be fermented en rosé. To create a rosé wine intentionally, the grapes, after being crushed and fermented on their skins for just sufficient time to extract enough colour, are then quickly pressed out. Therefore rosé may be made out of a mixture of black and white grapes, or entirely of black grapes.

Equipment for making wine

The plan of action that must be undertaken prior to the harvest is to gather together sufficient equipment to handle the output of the vineyard. This will not be necessary until the third season after planting, and the first vintage will be very light in comparison with those of later years; vines crop better year after year until they reach their sixth to eighth year and attain maturity and attendant full cropping capacity.

A wine press is a *must* for all vine growers possessed of more than a handful of vines, there are several small, simple presses on the market from £11·00–£48·00 for the small plantation. Alternatively, any carpenter can soon knock a wine press together, remembering to use good hard wood such as oak for the frame as it has to stand the pressure of some tons.

There is a larger 45 litre press on the market for £44·00, but for the vineyard of more than an acre a large hydraulic or electrically-operated press is required.

The next requirement is a fair sized half cask or two of a suitable size for the prospective crop in which the grapes can be trodden or crushed prior to going to the wine press. This is an essential process; if the berries were to be put into the press whole no juice would be obtained so they have to be broken or crushed, but gently, because the pips must not be broken or their acrid oil would spoil and taint the wine.

The age old customary and traditional method was that of treading grapes, and no doubt the constant action and friction warmed the grapes and encouraged a greater yield in the press with white grapes which are pressed out immediately. But nowadays one can buy admirable grape crushers or one can acquire a large old wooden roller mangle; the rollers can then be dismantled from their frame, and re-set horizontally into a V-shaped box constructed around them to form a hopper. The whole can then be fitted over a catch half cask or box below. Set the rollers close enough to crush every berry, yet not too close, or the pips will burst.

Expensive electrical equipment can be purchased to fulfill both the crushing and pressing tasks for the really large concern, the methods described above are for the smaller private venture, for the commercial undertaking such equipment would be neither practical nor economical.

Fermentation and storage containers

Here again the size of the vineyard dominates the capacity of the containers that will be required. At maturity the average outdoor vineyard vine yields from three to four pounds of fruit, some varieties will ripen considerably more; before maturity the crop will of course be lighter. Bearing in mind that it takes from about 15 lb. of grapes to produce one gallon of wine, an acre of vines can yield from 330 to 500 gallons, or 2,000–3,000 bottles of wine.

For the smaller vineyard, glass, earthenware and high density polythene vessels are first class for the fermenting and maturing of wine. These containers are made in $\frac{1}{2}$, 1 2, 5, and 10 gallon sizes, and are easily cleaned and handled. Good chestnut or oak casks are also excellent, perhaps the greater time and care in cleaning and sterilising them prior to use is outweighed by their ability to improve the quality of a wine, and their absorption of many of the less attractive elements. Wine does however evaporate in a cask, and must be frequently topped up to avoid souring and oxidising.

Commercially, large rigid fibre-class containers, ribbed black polythene vessels and glass-lined steel tanks are used. These are easily cleaned, and fitted with legs, cleaning hatches, and pressure gauges. These may be purchased in sizes ranging from 600–20,000 litre capacity to suit all possible requirements.

Other equipment

Also required will be one or two large polythene funnels, strainers, tubing for syphoning or racking the wine from one container to another to separate it from its deposit or lees without disturbing the latter, and some bored and solid jar or cask corks to fit the necks of the fermentation and storage vessels. Fermentation locks, one for each vessel will be needed, these are either of glass or plastic, and are in the form of a tube or a trap which is semi-filled with an SO_2 solution, and thus allows the carbon dioxide to escape, but in return allows no access of air or disease factors into the wine. They are fitted into the bored jar or cask corks.

Warning

Never, at any time, allow any metal equipment or container to come into contact with the wine, metals can seriously contaminate wine, and indeed some can render wine highly poisonous.

142

Sterilisation of equipment

Steps must be taken to ensure that all equipment is sufficiently sterilised immediately before it is used for processing the grape harvest.

There are several chemicals available that do this task admirably, namely sodium metabisulphite and potassium metabisulphite, and Campden tablets which can be crushed, between two spoons and mixed with water to form a sterilising agent; all give a sulphur dioxide solution.

Wooden half casks and the wine press should firstly be scrubbed with boiling water and soda, then rinsed down with a sterile solution before use. The remainder of the equipment must also be cleaned well and then rinsed with sterile solution. The latter can be made up by mixing 6% sulphur dioxide or three crushed Campden tablets per pint of water.

White wine production

Choose a fine bright day for the pressing operation bringing the grapes to the press as ripe as possible, every extra day of sun increases the sugar content.

Crush the bunches (a stout stake used as a "stomper" in a half cask is a fair method if you have no crusher) and make sure every berry is broken, for whole berries will not burst in the press.

Next transfer this pulp to the press as quickly as possible, pack the press barrel or "cheeses" firmly and steadily, the latter being squares of nylon mesh on which the pulp is packed, the four corners being folded over to create a strong flat envelope. These are piled one on another upwards from the press tray or platform; pack the cheeses squarely, thus avoiding having to unscrew the press and repack due to the load having squashed itself off centre as the pressure increases.

The juice will begin to run freely as the pulp is packed into the press, this juice makes the best wine and should be kept in separate containers from the juice obtained by pressure. When full pressure has been reached, leave the pressure on for some time, overnight if the press is a very large affair, attending at frequent intervals to the removal and sterilisation of the juice. As soon as each batch of juice leaves the press, it must immediately be treated with one Campden tablet per gallon, or with sodium metabisulphite, for it is essential that all undesirable wild yeasts and disease spores are eradicated at once before they can take hold and taint the wine.

Potential Alcohol Table

S.G. at 60°F.	Oechsle	Sugar content by weight per gallon		Potential alcohol percentage by volume
		lb.	ozs.	
1.130	130	3	0	17.3
1.125	125	2	14	16.7
1.120	120	2	13	16.0
1.115	115	2	11	15.2
1.110	110	2	10	14.5
1.105	105	2	8	13.9
1.100	100	2	6	13.4
1.095	95	2	4	12.6
1.090	90	2	2	12.0
1.085	85	2	0	11.2
1.080	80	1	13	10,5
1.075	75	1	11	9.7
1.070	70	1	9	9.0
1.065	65	1	7	8.4
1.060	60	1	5	7.7
1.055	55	1	3	7.0
1.050	50	1	1	6.4
1.045	45		14½	5.7
1.040	40		13	5.0
1.035	35		10	4.2
1.030	30		8	3.6
1.025	25		6	2.9
1.020	20		4	2.3
1.015	15		2	1.7
1.010	10			1.1
1.005	05			
1.000	00			
0.095	095			

Stand the stoppered juice in a temperature of between 50–60°F overnight, then the following morning the unwanted solid waste will have settled as a deposit, and the clear juice can be syphoned or racked from this deposit into a clean sterile container. Now take a reading of the specific gravity to determine the natural sugar content, and from this you will be able to ascertain whether or not any additional sugar is required. After this operation the "must" is ready to be dosed with the wine yeast starter to begin the fermentation.

Preparation of the yeast starter

Two or three days before the grape harvest, press out sufficient grapes to provide 1–2 pints of juice; bring this juice slowly to 160°F keeping it at this temperature for one minute in an aluminium, enamel or glass saucepan. Cool this now sterile liquid to 70–75°F, and pour it into a sterilised bottle adding a wine yeast of the same type as the grapes. There are a great many varieties of true wine yeast available today in dried, liquid and culture form, and in general one can obtain a suitable yeast for all the types of wine one hopes to create from home-grown grapes. Most of the varieties of white wine grape we grow in Great Britain are grown in the Rhine, Moselle and Alsatian vineyards, so a hock yeast would be acceptable, a champagne yeast can be used if a sparkling wine is required. A few yeast suppliers go further than this and offer Riesling, Sylvaner and Traminer yeasts, all of which are German and can be used for English wines.

Plug the top of the yeast starter bottle with a wad of cotton wool, and keep it in a warm room for two to three days to encourage a quick start to the fermentation.

Fermentation

After adding the starter to the grape juice, check the amount of sugar you calculated should be added, if any; an adjusted specific gravity reading of 75–80 oechsle resulting in a final alcohol content of 9.7–10.5 would require an initial sugar content of 1 lb. 13 ozs.–2 lb. An ideal sound alcohol content will result in a well balanced wine possessed of good keeping qualities. This would be the recommended initial sugar content to aim for, reference to the table shown in an earlier chapter will assist in working out the sugar required.

Refrain from adding the sugar until fermentation has started, a deep bed of sugar in the bottom of the jar can swamp and inhibit the yeast from starting quickly. If the amount of sugar needed is 1 lb. or more, it is wiser to add half after the beginning of the ferment, and the second half some three or four weeks later after the first racking.

Next fit a sterilised bored cork and fermentation lock, filling the U-bend or cavity with Campden solution to prevent disease from attacking the wine. Keep the young wine in a cool temperature of between 50–60°F to encourage a steady, slow fermentation, which makes for a better quality wine eventually than a wine reared in a higher temperature.

Racking

Within three to four weeks the initial vigorous fermentation will die down due to most of the sugar having been used in the creation of alcohol, and carbon dioxide, which is the gas which forces its way out through the fermentation trap. The wine will have formed a substantial sediment or lees consisting of dead and dying yeast cells and unwanted solid matter. The wine must now be racked off this lees. The wine itself will let you know when this is necessary by the formation of a solid layer of lees, a dawning of clarification throughout the wine, and the sudden funereal place of the gas escaping through the air-lock. The wine must now be racked off the lees into a fresh sterile jar followed by a reading of the specific gravity to compare the present reading with that taken last. Reference to the hydrometer table will indicate the degree of the conversion of the sugar into alcohol. After racking now is the time to add the second half of the sugar if the initial sugar content required a larger contribution added in two doses.

Acidity

To recap on the problem of sugar additions to a grape juice: in a good year when the initial specific gravity reading is high, from 75-85 oechsle, no additional sugar is required and the wine will not be over acid and requires no dilution with a sugar and water syrup to dilute acidity; however, in an average year each gallon of wine must be diluted with

one fifth of the total volume with 20% syrup (1/5th gallon
of water plus 6 ozs. sugar), plus a further 6 ozs. of sugar to
bring up the specific gravity of the juice. In a bad year, the
acidity level will be higher and the natural sugar content
considerably lower, so that 25% of the volume of each gallon
of wine will be added as 20% syrup (one quart of water
plus 8 ozs. of sugar), plus a further 9–12 ozs. of sugar to bring
the sugar content up to a reasonable level. The exact amount
of sugar you need can be ascertained from the specific gravity
table in the previous chapter, this has been explained earlier.
The syrup additions are mentioned so that those makers of
grape wine interested in obtaining a well balanced wine in a
poor or an average year when the acid level is too pronounced
can adjust their wines accordingly.

An alternative method of reducing acidity in a grape
juice is by the use of precipitated chalk (calcium carbonate).
B.P. In an average season no more than ½–1 oz. per 10 gallons
should be needed, whereas in a very poor year as much as
4 ozs. per gallon could be required. One part by weight of
precipitated chalk will precipitate 1½ parts of tartaric acid,
it is better to err on an under, rather than an overdose, as
acidity can drop naturally of its own accord during maturation .

Mix the precipitated chalk, let us say ½ oz. in an average
season for 10 gallons, very well with a little water in a small
bottle then release it into the wine. Give it time to settle out,
then taste the wine, and if it is still very acid the same dose
could be applied once more, in this way over-application may
be avoided.

Secondary fermentation

The secondary fermentation is a steady, quiet affair
compared with the headstrong vigour of the first ferment.
The wine must now permanently be kept in the cool, from
50–60°F, and will slowly clarify as the fermentation draws to a
close. A month or two after the last racking, lees will again have
formed and the wine must again be racked off to prevent
spoilage from "off" flavours given by the decaying matter in
the lees. When the fermentation ceases completely, and the
S.G. indicates that all the sugar has been consumed by showing
a reading of 995 or thereabouts, the fermentation lock should

be removed, the wine racked if necessary, and a solid cork rammed home before the wine is again stored away in the cool to mature.

Storage and maturing

An important point to remember at this stage in the production of wine is that all containers, be they glass or wood, must be kept filled right up to the bung, for wine can only go bad in the presence of air. In casks evaporation and absorption are continuous, so attention must be given to this frequently. The wine should be kept right up to the bottom of the cork or bung at all times, for in the air are spores of mycoderma vini and other evil bacteria which are ever ready to strike and turn the precious wine to vinegar. The quality of the vintage in question will determine the length of storage time required; even a poor wine will benefit from bulk storage, but the improvement will not be startling. Such a wine may be bottled at any time from six months to 18 months old—an average wine will benefit by storage of 18 months to two years, and the very best wines made in that one year in 10 when the sun shines continuously for months on end, the vintage year, then two to three years is recommended, but no more.

Clarifying

If a wine proves difficult to clear naturally, and it should be almost clear two months after being pressed, there are several methods that can be adopted to encourage clarity.

The easiest method is to put the wine out for a night or two during frosty weather which should immediately precipitate all the offending hazy particles. This can be done during the first winter, or indeed if the wine is still undergoing a longer bulk maturation, during the second or third winter if necessary.

Another method is to use white of egg. To every 10 gallons of wine or less beat one egg white until it is stiff, then mix in and dissolve the egg in one gallon of the wine. Pour this treated gallon of wine into the main bulk of the wine mixing well to ensure an even distribution. After a period of 10 days syphon off the wine into a fresh sterile container, if a cask, fumigate it well first with sulphur, and the wine will come clear leaving its deposits behind.

There are many proprietary wine finings on the market, and one which has proved exceptionally useful is Bentonite, providing the instructions for use are followed carefully.

It should be made clear here, however, that a wine should clear naturally and quickly, only if it should prove stubborn is there any need to resort to the foregoing methods.

Bottling

Use only proper wine bottles as all other bottles are both unsafe and unsuitable. The majority of British white grape wines are certain to be of Hock, Moselle or Alsatian style, so these are the most applicable type of bottle. Hock bottles are brown, Moselle green, and Alsatian wines are bottled in either colour and are usually a little bigger. Any well-cleaned wine bottle will suffice, but it is more pleasing to the eye and the aesthetic sense of the beholder when a wine is served in the correct bottle.

The bottles must be cleaned well, first in hot water and liquid soap washing up liquid, then rinsed well, followed by a further rinse in a sterile solution of sulphur dioxide and then rinsed again in hot water. Allow them to drain and dry out before use.

Corks must be proper cylindrical 2″ straight wine corks to keep the wine sound and unspoilt during bottle storage. Before use soften them by placing them in a bowl of boiling water, and immediately before use dip them into a sterile solution to eliminate all possible trouble. For the smaller concern a metal lever hand corker is fine enabling one to squeeze the corks sufficiently before ramming them into the bottles. A larger bench model with fitted stand for the bottle can be acquired for the larger establishment, the action and working parts are the same as the above.

The bottles must be filled to just within the height of the cork from the top of the bottle to allow the cork to be forced right down on to the wine, thus eliminating any air gap and subsequent spoilage.

If a fair storage period in bottle is foreseen, the bottle tops may be dipped in melted paraffin wax which keeps the corks fit, damp and insect free. Alternatively, coloured viscose (plastic) capsules can be fitted over the top of the bottle neck, they prove useful as vintage identification by using a different colour capsule each year—it is useful to be able to immediately recognise the vintage without having to take bottles out to read the label for the date. Store bottles on their sides to prevent the corks from drying out.

Red wine production

Grapes for red wine benefit by being as ripe as possible before harvesting, for the longer they are exposed to the sun the greater will be the sugar content, and in consequence the wine will be more alcoholic, it will keep better and have more body, and the acidity will be lower. November is not too late, even late November if the grapes are sound, in a really sunless season some varieties have been harvested as late as mid-December, but if the weather is against you and the grapes are beginning to go mouldy and spoil, then they must be picked at once, ripe or not. Cut the grapes when they are dry, free from dew, and if possible on a fine bright day; wet grapes never make a good wine.

Pick the grapes into clean baskets, then crush them on the lines suggested for white wines. The initial fermentation is conducted on the skins. According to the gallonage of the vintage, large plastic dustbins, earthenware tubs, casks with one end knocked out, carboys or modern fibre-glass settling or fermenting cylinders may be used after adequate sterilisation, the temperature of the room must be from 60–65°F., so that the juice quickly adjusts itself to this temperature. The "must" is immediately sterilised by mixing in two Campden tablets per gallon, or 0.1 oz. of sulphur dioxide (potassium metabisulphite) in solution per 10 gallons; this checks all unwanted ferments and disease spores that would otherwise spoil the wine. Cover the "must" with muslin under a thick layer of doubled blanketing, and leave the juice to warm up and purify under the influence of the sterilising solution.

Yeast starter

Three or four days prior to harvesting, a yeast starter must be prepared on the lines recommended in the previous section dealing with white wines. In this case the choice of yeast type will be different, for red wines the choice varies from Burgundy, Claret, Beaujolais and Port, so one can suit the yeast to the prospective type and quality of the wine in question. Before adding the yeast starter to the wine, take a reading of the specific gravity with the hydrometer; in a good season the reading will be fairly high, but in an average or poor season the reading will be low, representing too low a sugar content to create a sound wine without the addition of some extra sugar. A red wine will require a natural or adjusted initial S.G. of from 75–85 oechsle, or even as high as 95 oechsle; so before adding the sugar make up the sugar content to this level by referring to the S.G./sugar tables in the previous section on white wines, and act accordingly. Once the "must" has warmed up, stir in the yeast starter well, and recover the vessel.

The object of the exercise here is to ferment the grapes on their skins long enough for a decent robust colour to be extracted, and character and body may be drawn from the pulp of the grapes, then the wine may be drawn off and fermented on alone. There are several hazards that must be coped with along this early stage of the proceedings. The most important being that this first vigorous fermentation causes the skins and pulp to form a "cap" over the must, and if this cap is not pushed down into the wine many times daily with a wooden tool, the pulp will acetify, and turn the wine bad and sour. Alternatively, a perforated wooden disc could be made to slot down well below the surface of the wine, and hold the pulp forcibly below the surface. Secondly, the top of this vessel, or vessels, must at all times be kept well covered either with a bung and fermentation lock or with muslin and several layers of thick blanketing to keep all fruit or vinegar flies and airborne bacteria spores at bay. If these two points are strictly adhered to, being a vigorous ferment, the layer of carbon dioxide gas produced by the fermenting wine will keep the "must" healthy, and the colour and character will be extracted from the grapes quickly and efficiently.

Secondary fermentation

When the S.G. reading drops to 10oe., draw the wine from pulp while there is residual sugar left to conduct the secondary fermentation; if the must has been in a cask then this is a simple matter of drawing the wine out through the tap. Again here the free run juice will be superior, so keep this separate from the last of the juice which should be drawn from the pulp in the wine press. After pressing, release the screw, stir up the pulp and press again to obtain every possible ounce of wine from the pulp.

Red wine benefits greatly from being fermented and stored in cask, the wood both gives character and a certain quality to the wine, and at the same time extracts any excess harshness. The warning here is to keep the containers, casks in particular, checked every fortnight for evaporation, and top up if necessary, for it is at this time when fermentation is slow and little carbon dioxide is being given off that troubles are most likely to strike.

Thereafter continue as for white wine, but remember always to bottle in green bottles; there are two types available, firstly, the gradual sloping shouldered Burgundy bottles for heavier wines and the sharper shouldered longer necked claret bottles for the lighter wines. There is good reason behind the use of dark bottles for red wine, if it were to be bottled in clear bottles it would quickly lose its depth of colour, and thus much of its attraction.

If a really strong red wine is required to each gallon add 4 ozs. of sugar when the S.G. drops to the vicinity of 10oe. To do this, start with the wine at the recommended S.G., and keeping a close watch on the S.G. reading throughout the development period of the wine, add 4 ozs. of sugar after racking off the wine. When the wine again drops, this time to 0oe, rack, and follow this quickly by adding a further 4 ozs. sugar. This can be repeated yet a third time, but do it very carefully adding just a spoon at first to see if the wine reacts by beginning to ferment again. If so, then add the 4 ozs., but if not, then the yeast has expired and any excess sugar will render the wine a sickly, sweet syrup. The object of this exercise is to make a strong Port style wine with an alcohol content in the region of 17–19%, and such practises need great care and patience.

Vin rosé

This can be made by adding a few black grapes of known strong pigmentation, for example Seibel 13053, to a white fermentation, and removing them when sufficient colour has been extracted. Elderberries are an excellent substitute, and were in fact used in Portugal for this very purpose until fairly recently when this practice was officially stopped. No doubt elderberries were used elsewhere in Europe from time to time when extra colour was required!

Alternatively the initial black grape pulp fermentation can be continued for just long enough for sufficient colour to have been expressed for a Rosé wine, then the wine is quickly drawn off, and the pulp pressed out as before.

Secondary wine from grape Pomace

A light and acceptable wine for every day consumption may be made by steeping the dry cake of grape skins as removed from the wine press. Put this pulp into a large closable vessel, cover the pomace with warm water, and then add sufficient sterilising agent per gallon to kill off all bacteria. Allow a period of 24 hours to elapse to let the sulphur gas off, then add a vigorous yeast starter to the pulp. Steep strong-flavoured grapes for 24 hours, and mild grapes for 48 hours before pressing out the pulp once again. It is 100% essential to keep the pulp submerged during the steeping period, preferably with a perforated wooden disc of the same interior diameter as the container.

After pressing, add sufficient sugar to bring the adjusted oechsle reading up to 75 or 80. This secondary wine will be very much weaker and drier than the first pressing, so a fair amount of sugar will have to be added.

CHAPTER 12

The year in the vineyard, vinery and winery

A month by month plan of action

THE viticultural year begins in December and not in January for it is in the former month that indoor vines are pruned, the first of the year's tasks.

December

In the vineyard

There is luckily little to do in the vineyard in December; there is little point in digging yet for the outdoor vines should be pruned in January resulting in constant walking all over the vineyard.

In the vinery

Keep all ventilators and windows open to allow the vines to "winter." Mid-month prune all vines, and spray with tar oil afterwards. Begin renovating border around the vines, and applying manure, bone meal, wood ash, and fertiliser, etc. . . . and fumigate with anti-mildew and anti-insect smoke bombs.

In the winery

Rack new wines as and when necessary, moving wine into cooler atmosphere once first fermentation has elapsed into secondary ferment.

January

In the vineyard

Prune all vines, and when conditions permit in southerly locations plant out cuttings into a sand-lined trench. Elsewehere keep cuttings in boxes of damp sand until March. Once pruning has been completed, digging or cultivation can begin.

In the vinery

Keep all ventilators and windows open. Continue to tend to the border; fumigate again against mildew and insect pests. Start bench grafting, and where propagating frame is available strike cuttings and vine eyes in pots and turves.

In the winery

Rack new wines when necessary, any new or older wine that proves stubborn in clearing can be subjected to a frost for a night or two, which should help.

February

In the vineyard

Once cuttings are planted, the vineyard can be dug when weather permits. Tighten slack wires, renew rotten posts, etc.

In the vinery

Continue to keep all ventilators and windows open. Apply lime to border if necessary, and complete any leftover winter chores.

In the winery

Rack new wines as necessary, check over all maturing wines to make sure the wine is up to the cork level, and renew old corks, rack if necessary. Once fermentation ceases, make sure that the jars are completely full, fit them with solid corks and stand away in the dark and cool to mellow and mature.

March

In the vineyard

Complete digging operations. In colder areas plant out cutings into sand lined trenches, and finish all winter chores. Plant out new or replacement vines.

In the vinery

Now the weather is warmer keep windows and ventilators open; see to glass and woodwork repairs, repairing any broken panes, repairing putty and painting if necessary. Tighten wires if slack, and drop bearers on to the border or path if possible to ensure an even bud break next month.

Start to provide heat for late ripening varieties, shutting up windows and ventilators in this section, and keep the border, path and vines damp.

In the winery

Begin to look out those wines that are due for bottling; those of an effervescent nature are ideally bottled in April when they are apt to come to life slightly with the advent of spring, and to trap this elusive quality in bottle is highly desirable. Clean and sterilize the necessary bottles in readiness. Rack wines that require it.

April

In the vineyard

Complete the planting of new vines. This is the ideal month for grafting on to rooted stocks in the open when the warm weather moves in permanently.

In the vinery

Once bud break threatens, shut up the house, and damp the border, path and vines to encourage an even break. Allow shoots to show if they are good or bad croppers before pinching out the lesser shoots from each spur.

In the winery

Bottle any wines that are ready and would benefit from spring bottling. To ensure complete stability and brilliant clarity, run wine through a filtration plant before bottling.

May

In the vineyard

In May the buds break and shoot, before thinning the buds to one per nine or so inches, wait to see which are carrying a good crop of fruit and then remove the poorer shoots. Keep vineyard well hoed and weeded. Water cuttings if necessary.

In the vinery

In general the shoots are long enough to tie in early this month to the wires; keep the house clean and airy by day, but close up at night in case of May frost. Keep a watch in a wet spring for mildew and powder at once if it appears, preferably keeping a light dusting of powder on the vines at all times.

June

In the vineyard

Tuck or tie in the young shoots as they gain sufficient height to prevent their being snapped off in the wind. Keep the ground open and clean by a regular hoeing programme; dedication to this task at this time means fewer weeds later in the season and next year.

In the vinery

Vines in the cold-house flower in June. During the later stages of flowering pinch out the tips of the shoots four or five leaves beyond the last flower spray, also pinch out all sub-laterals. Follow this operation immediately by hand pollinating each vine with pollen from other vines preferably. Air house well in the mornings; after pollination at mid-day close the house, and spray floor and border to raise humidity After blossom has set, resume liquid feeding and watering, but do not spray vines any more with water, for the remainder of the growing season.

July

In the vineyard

According to whether the spring has been early or late, the vines will flower some time this month. During an advanced stage in flowering and on a fine day go around each vine and pinch out the growing tip of each flowering lateral eight leaves above the last bunch, and pinch out all sub-laterals to encourage a good set. Give each vine a kick or a good shake to spread the pollen. Continue tying or tucking in the laterals as necessary, and tie the replacement canes as they lengthen. Keep up the hoeing programme, and start the anti-mildew campaign now.

In the vinery

Thin the grapes with a pair of grape thinning scissors. De-shoot the sub-laterals constantly for all energy must be channelled into grape production. Water as necessary and apply liquid fertilizer. Keep up a powdering of Bordeaux and sulphur powder to repel mildew attack.

August

In the vineyard

Continue with the elimination of sub-laterals on both bearers and replacement canes. Pinch out the top of the latter when they reach the top of their canes. Keep earth aerated by regular hoeing, and keep up spraying or powdering against mildew.

In the vinery

Continue with the removal of sub-laterals, and watering and feeding when necessary until the black grapes being to colour, and the white to turn translucent ("veraison"), when all feeding and watering must cease immediately. In a really good season the earliest cold-house grape varieties can ripen sufficiently to be edible by late August. Stop mildew precautions as grapes ripen.

September

In the vineyard

Continue as suggested for August; make preparations for protecting the grapes against the ravages of the birds and wasps, preferably with netting, and put this in place well before the grapes ripen. Stop mildew repellent as grapes ripen.

In the vinery

Harvest continues; take care now to shut the house at night to trap the remaining absorbed day-time warmth to assist the later varieties to ripen. Watch for wasp and bird damage, and take necessary steps if trouble arrives. Start heat for hot-house grapes now.

In the winery

Clean and prepare all winemaking equipment, if necessary bottle off older wines to free containers for the new wine.

October

In the vineyard

The earlier varieties of wine grapes ripen in October, but before rushing to gather the harvest when it *looks* ripe, do take the trouble to take a reading of the specific gravity of the grape juice, either with a hydrometer or a refractometer, to see if there is sufficient natural sugar present to create a palatable wine that will keep well. This is well worth while. Providing they are sound and mildew free, the longer grapes can hang on the vine, the greater the eventual sugar content and the better the resultant wine.

In the vinery

As September; the later cold-house grapes should be ripening now. Should they prove reluctant to do so, supply some heat if possible, being particularly sure to shut the house up in mid-afternoon to keep as much of the day heat inside as possible. On fine days air the house well to prevent mildew.

In the winery

Choose a fine day for harvesting the grapes, and sterilise all equipment prior to use. For white wine, crush the grapes prior to pressing, sterilise the resultant juice, stand overnight, rack the wine from the sediment, add wine yeast and ferment. With red wine, tread or crush the grapes, sterilise the must and after 24 hours add the wine yeast and ferment on the skins for sufficient time to extract sufficient flavour and colour. Then strain from the pulp and ferment wine in closed containers with air-locks; press out the pulp for second-class wine.

November

In the vineyard

Vintage continues for later ripening varieties of grapes. When harvest has been completed, winter cultivation can begin. Ideally the soil should be thrown from the channels between the vines' rows over on to the vine rows themselves semi-covering the stems. In most cases apply manure or compost every other season, and apply lime in the alternate years either now or in February.

In the vinery

Once the last bunch of grapes is cut, cut off all heat, open all windows and ventilators permanently, and begin winter chores, clearing out leaves and burning them, cleaning out house, beginning the border renovation, repairing and painting, etc; the more that is done now means less in the spring when one is always more busy.

In the winery

Continue to convert the remaining grapes into wine when they are ready, rack the October wines as soon as they begin to clear and throw a worthwhile sediment. Keep wines in a warmer atmosphere during the primary ferment, and move them into a cooler place for the secondary fermentation.

CHAPTER 13

Winegrowing in the European Economic Community

The English Vineyards Association has drawn up some notes on important points relevant to Commercial Wine Production within the E.E.C., the more important of which are mentioned here. Private vineyards are not subject to the following rulings where the resultant wine is not offered for sale.

There are no restrictions forbidding the planting of vineyards in England.

Vine Varieties

Quality wines can only be produced from Vitis Vinifera species recommended or authorised by each member state. Vine varieties not included among those listed must be eliminated from each individual vineyard intended for the production of Quality Wines. (An exception will be made to this condition for just three years, provided that the alien vine varieties belong to V. Vinifera species and they do not exceed 20% of the total plantation).

Recommended Vines

Varieties which are cultivated in the Community now and which belong to the species V. Vinifera; cultivars which are descended from interspecific crosses whose suitability for cultivation is recognised as being satisfactory in providing wines the good quality of which is recognised.

Authorised Vines

This includes varieties which produce a sound, saleable wine of reasonable quality although inferior to that referred to above.

Temporarily Authorised Vines

This category covers vine varieties which do not fall within either of the two above denominations, but which are still of some economic importance, and those whose cultivation is not entirely satisfactory.

To Conclude. . .

Where applicable, quality shall be judged on the basis of results from tests on the suitability for cultivation of the vine varieties in question, and on the results of analytical and sensory tests on the wine concerned. A list of vines considered suitable for the production of English wine will be made available to members of the English Vineyards Association. The exclusion of any specific variety does not mean that it may not be planted, simply that wine made from it cannot be offered for sale. Also, this list may at any time be extended to include new varieties should they be properly justified on all counts.

To qualify for v.q.p.r.d., (English equivalent being the authorised seal of quality), it will be necessary to limit the quantity of grapes harvested per acre. Each member state is obliged to determine this figure and will be required to take into account yields obtained over the previous ten years. Any excess will automatically eliminate the vineyard from the qualification of v.q.p.r.d.

Finally, cultivation practises such as irrigation will be subject to control.

Regulations Regarding Wine Production

The processing of grapes into must, and from must into wine, intended for the production of quality wine, shall be effected within the specified regions where the grapes were harvested, except under certain conditions authorised by the member state, and vinification methods for the production of quality wines will be subject to control.

Quality wines are required to show a minimum alcoholometric strength, to be determined by each member state, and based on an average taken from ten years of satisfactory harvests. Alcoholometric strength for quality wines in the United Kingdom must not be less than 6% by volume.

The increase in strength permitted by each member state by the addition of sucrose in water solution is only permitted until 30th June 1979, and may only involve an increase of 10% in the volume of the product.

Conditions and limits concerning acidification and deacidification of the grape in its various stages of processing, together with sweetening of quality wines will also be subject to controls.

Producers shall be required to submit their wines likely to benefit from the denomination v.q.p.r.d. to an organoleptical test subject to the limits defined by each member state.

List of Factors Capable of Being Taken into Account in the Testing of Quality Wine

A. Determined on the basis of an organoleptical test:

    1. Colour
    2. Clarity and deposit
    3. Smell and taste

B. Determined on the basis of tests of wine behaviour:

    4. Behaviour in air
    5. Behaviour in cold

C. Determined on the basis of a microbiological test:

    6. Behaviour in a drying cabinet
    7. Appearance of wine and deposit

D. Determined on the basis of a physical and chemical analysis:

    8. Density
    9. Degree of Alcohol

10. Total dry extract (obtained by Densimetry)
11. Reducing sugars
12. Sucrose
13. Ash
14. Alkalinity of ash
15. Total acidity
16. Volatile acidity
17. Fixed acidity
18. pH
19. Free sulphurous anhydride ⎫
20. Total sulphurous anhydride ⎬ Sulphur dioxide
 ⎭

E. Determined on the basis of an additional analysis:

21. Carbonic acid (semi sparkling and sparkling wines at 20°C.)

RULES CONCERNING OENOLOGICAL PRACTICES IN WINE PRODUCTION

The increase of alcohol content for white wines produced in G.B. may be up to 3.5°, and in the case of red wines to 4° until 31st January 1980, this being on condition that the natural alcohol content is at least 5°. For years during which the climatic conditions have been exceptionally unfavourable, the permitted increase may be 1° greater. This addition of sucrose may only be effected by dry sugaring, or until 30th June 1979 in aqueous solution, provided that the total volume is not increased by more than 15%.

Fresh grapes, grape must, partially fermented must and young wine still undergoing fermentation may be subject to de-acidification, but not to the addition of acid.

RULES CONCERNING LABELS AND PRESENTATION

It is advised that readers consult the Ministry of Agriculture on the current ruling on the size, format and wording required for wine labels. Probably it will be necessary to indicate the fluid ounce capacity of the container, the alcohol content of the wine, and either the name and address of the bottler of the wine, or a pre-arranged code number. For further details apply to the Ministry of Agriculture, Fisheries and Food, (for the attention of the department dealing with E.E.C. Regulations), Whitehall, London, SW1A 2HH.

APPENDIX

VINE SUPPLIERS

The undermentioned are all very busy people, and cannot contend with chance callers. A stamped self-addressed envelope will bring you all the information on the vines grown or imported by each individual, or an appointment to call may be made by post or telephone.

BERKSHIRE—HOME COUNTIES

W. L. Cardy, Esq., Lower Bowden, Pangbourne, Berkshire. Tel.: Pangbourne 2878.

Vines: Ortega, Müller Thurgau, Seyve-Villard, Reichensteiner.

B. H. Theobald, Esq., Westbury Farm, Purley, Reading, Berkshire. Tel.: Pangbourne 3123.

Vines: Madeleine Angevine, Müller Thurgau, Seibel 13053, Seigerrebe, Scheurebe and Seyve-Villard, six others on trial.

DEVON—SOMERSET—WEST COUNTRY

Miss G. G. Pearkes, Rhyll Manor, Dulverton, Somerset. Tel.: Anstey Mills 225. An experimental private vineyard where some 90 vine varieties are on trial and many recognised forms of training and pruning form a living demonstration.

Vines: Gewurztraminer, Grenache, Madeleine Angevine, Müller Thurgau, Madeleine Sylvaner, Ortega, Perle, four Pinots, Précoce de Malingre, Riesling, Reichensteiner, Seigerrebe, Scheurebe, Sylvaner, Seyve-Villard, Traminer and many others for outdoor and indoor cultivation.

ESSEX—HOME COUNTIES

J. G. & I. M. Barrett, The Vineyards, Cricks Green, Felsted, Essex. Tel.: Great Leighs 504.

Vines: Unrooted vine cuttings for sale, many varieties. Minimum order of 100 cuttings accepted from December, Spring delivery. Discounts available for quantities and for collection of order.

APPENDIX

HAMPSHIRE—WILTSHIRE

J. R. M. Donald, Esq., The Garden House, West Tytherley, Nr. Salisbury, Wiltshire. Tel.: 0794 40644.

Vines: Ascot Citronelle, Madeleine Angevine, Madeleine Royale, Müller Thurgau, Seibel 13053, Triomphe d'Alsace and White Frontignan.

SUFFOLK—EAST ANGLIA

B. T. Ambrose, Esq., Nether Hall, Cavendish, Suffolk. Tel.: Glemsford 221 & 395.

Vines: Imported Müller Thurgau ex Alsace, order in the autumn, spring delivery.

SURREY—SOUTH EAST

A. Massel & Co. Ltd., Weare Street, Ockley, Surrey. Tel.: Oakwood Hill 441 & 477.

Vines: All grafted on to American rootstock:

White Varieties: Bacchus 133, Faber, Forta 100, Friesamer, Huxelrebe, Mariensteiner, Müller Thurgau, Ortega, Perle, Reichensteiner, Rieslaner, Scheurebe and Seigerrebe.

Black Varieties: Kolor, Pinot Noir, Zweight Rebe.

Hybrids: Seyve-Villard, (white), and Seibel 13053, (red).

INDEX

INDEX

INDEX

INDEX

Other 'AW' Books

C. J. J. Berry

"130 NEW WINEMAKING RECIPES"

—the companion volume to "First Steps in Winemaking," giving an unrivalled collection of recipes for modern materials (dried fruits, concentrates, etc.). 50 sparkling cartoons by Rex Royle   (30p)
                    postage 6p. (Canada and U.S.A. $1.25 incl. postage)

Edited by C. J. J. Berry

"AMATEUR WINEMAKER" RECIPES

—this "A.W." book contains a fascinatingly varied collection of over 200 recipes garnered from several years' issues of the wine-maker's favourite magazine, including many by that well-known Birmingham winemaker, Cyril Shave. It includes many unusual herb and other wines and a particularly good set of recipes for liqueurs, punches, fruit cups and party drinks. The cartoons are by Rex Royle. (35p) postage 6p. (Canada and U.S.A. $1.25 inc. postage)

C. J. J. Berry

"HOME-BREWED BEERS AND STOUTS"

—the first and best full-length book on the subject. How to brew your own delicious lager, pale ale, bitter, mild, brown, stout or extra stout. Fully illustrated   (30p) postage 6p.
                    (Canada and U.S.A. $1.25 incl. postage)

C. J. J. Berry

"HINTS ON HOME BREWING"

—a "rapid course" on home brewing, but containing all the would be brewer needs to know. Illustrated (15p) postage 4p. (75c. inc. postage)

B. Acton and P. Duncan

"MAKING WINES LIKE THOSE YOU BUY"

—how, with your own materials and equipment, to make wines every bit as good as those you have enjoyed on the Continent: Red and White Table Wine, Sauternes, Hock, Moselle, Chianti, Port, Sherry, Madeira, etc., etc. Full range of home-made liqueurs as well. A fascinating book taking you into the finer points of winemaking. Fully illustrated   (35p) postage 6p.
                    (Canada and U.S.A. $1.25 incl. postage)

J. Restall and D. Hebbs

"HOW TO MAKE WINES WITH A SPARKLE"

—if you follow its methods and principles you too can produce impressive sparkling wines which will be the envy and admiration of your winemaking friends.   (50p) postage 6p.

P. Duncan and B. Acton

"PROGRESSIVE WINEMAKING"

—advanced winemaking dealt with by these two popular authors in a readable and fascinating way. This is a really fat volume of some 500 pages which is really two books in one—Part I deals with the scientific theory of winemaking. Part II deals with the production of quality wines, both red and white, and the making of sherry, port, and Madeira type wines, and sparkling wines—all in the greatest detail.   Paperback 75p, post 10p. ($3 post free)
Hard covers £1.25, post 12p. ($5 post free)

"JUDGING HOME-MADE WINES"

—the handbook of the National Guild of Judges; constitution, notes for judges, judges' stewards and show organisers. *How to Judge,* specimen show schedules, etc., etc. Invaluable for those organising competitions   (25p) postage 4p (80c. incl. postage)

C. J. J. Berry

"WINEMAKING WITH CANNED AND DRIED FRUIT"

—the latest and simplest winemaking method of all. All you need is a can-opener! How to make wine from tinned fruits and juices, concentrates, jams, jellies and dried fruit easily obtainable from your grocer or supermarket. Cut out all the drudgery and make wine the easy way.   (35p) postage 6p

Ken Shales

"BREWING BETTER BEERS"

—a lively book on home brewing by that master of the Craft, Ken Shales, of Basildon (which is likely to be renamed Boozledon, it seems!). This book gives Ken's personal, well tried recipes for all types of malt liquor, from palest lager to extra stout. and explains many of the finer points of technique to enable you to formulate your own recipes   (30p) postage 6p
(Canada and U.S.A. $.25 incl. postage)

B. Acton and P. Duncan

"MAKING MEAD"

—these two popular authors tell you how to make the oldest alcoholic drink of all, to say nothing of Hippocras, Metheglin, Cyser, Pyments, Melomels and Honey Beers. A book with a lively, fresh approach to an unjustly neglected aspect of winemaking. Illustrated
(35p) postage 6p (Canada and U.S.A. $1.25 incl. postage)

T. Edwin Belt

"PRESERVING WINEMAKING INGREDIENTS"

—another recent "AW" book, and the only one available dealing with this aspect of winemaking. It tells how, in times of plenty or surplus, to preserve fruit, flowers and vegetables for use later in the year, when time and utensils are available. It deals in detail with preservation by means of drying (how to dry, for instance, rosehips, elderberries, sloes, bilberries, apples, etc., etc.), chemical preservation, deep freezing and chunk bottling. Also how to make syrups, jams and jellies from wild and garden fruit. (35p)

postage 6p

J. R. Mitchell
"SCIENTIFIC WINEMAKING—MADE EASY"

—this is the book that every serious and ambitious winemaker has been waiting for; it is easily the most advanced yet down-to-earth manual available. It deals in detail with the chemistry of wine, but it also sets out for you a wealth of valuable information. It has a wonderful chapter of detailed recipes for making specific types of fruit wines, and another excellent one on the simple tests that a winemaker can use to ensure wines of perfect balance and highest quality. Written by a scientist who specialises in quality control, it will open your eyes to the possibilities of improvement that a little scientific knowledge can bring to your winemaking. 260 pages

(60p) postage 8p